W9-CCB-095

RIFLES
SMALL &ARMS

RIFLES
SMALL &ARMS

BARNES & NOBLE BOOKS

NEW YORK

This edition published by Barnes & Noble, Inc.,
by arrangement with Book Sales, Inc.

2004 Barnes & Noble Books

This edition produced for sales in the U.S.A., its
territories, and dependencies only.

Copyright © 2004 Quintet Publishing Limited
All rights reserved. No part of this publication may be
reproduced, stored in a retrieval system or transmitted
in any form or by any means, electronic, mechanical,
photocopying, recording or otherwise, without the
permission of the copyright holder.

M 10 9 8 7 6 5 4 3 2 1

ISBN 0-7607-6231-7

This book was designed and produced by
Quintet Publishing Limited
6 Blundell Street
London N7 9BH

Designed and Edited by Q2A Solutions

Publisher: Ian Castello-Cortes
Associate Publisher: Laura Price
Creative Director: Richard Dewing

Art Director: Roland Codd
Project Editors: Jenny Doubt, Catherine Osborne

Manufactured in Singapore by Provision Pte Ltd
Printed in Singapore by Star Standard Industries (Pte) Ltd

The material used in this publication previously appeared in
Encyclopedia of Rifles and Handguns by S. Connolly, *The Illustrated
Encyclopedia of Firearms* by I.V. Hogg, *Handguns* by F. Wilkinson,
and *Rifles and Handguns* by R. Adam.

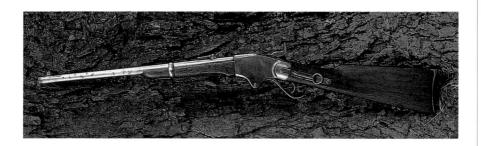

Contents

Introduction

"So long as the infantry had a smooth-bore musket, and had thus no precision in action beyond 100 paces, it was little inclined to exact scientific researches. But the precision and the long range of the rifled weapon, and in particular the improvement of it due to various breech-loading systems, compelled the infantry to occupy themselves seriously with the trajectory, in order to see how far the precision and the range could be improved and the best possible infantry arm be obtained."
Letters on Artillery VII: Prince Kraft zu Hohenlohe-Ingelfingen, 1887.

In many ways the arrival of gunpowder — with its power to propel projectiles — ushered in the modern era. The first European hand guns helped cannons blow holes in medieval notions of warfare.

Renaissance craftsmen refined these weapons, making them more portable and accurate, while gifted inventors such as Leonardo da Vinci laid the groundwork for quicker and safer means of igniting the charge. At the same time, what had once been strictly military weaponry gradually became domestic. These early weapons, with their hand-tooled workings and intricate markings, were prized by their original owners just as they are now, in the hands of collectors.

The rifle reversed this trend when it was developed first as a personal weapon, and then proved itself in the field of battle. Imparting a spin to a discharged bullet increased its accuracy, and hunters were among the first to benefit from this advance. In the conflicts of the eighteenth and nineteenth centuries, these new weapons spelt superiority in the arms race. Many subsequent rifle developments were inspired or refined in combat.

The study of rifles and handguns acknowledges the brilliance of those who left their mark on gun-making, and on history itself. Many of these names have become emblematic of their age: von Dreyse, Forsyth, Ferguson, Colt, Remington, Smith and Wesson, Beretta, Luger, and Mauser.

Some of the intensity of these innovators is reflected in the passions of those now involved with rifles and

Right **The ancestries of the powerful .44in Magnum Smith & Wesson Model 29 (top) and Ruger Super Redhawk (bottom) can be traced back to the Smith & Wesson .44's of the late 1800s (middle).**

handguns. Collectors recognize the beauty and rarity not only of the guns themselves, but of the ammunition, gun cases, and advertisements relating to rifles and handguns. These passions spill over into the use of weapons in target shooting contests and in the resurgence of hand-crafted weapons and ammunition. In a sense history has gone full-circle, with some modern producers attending to their weapons with a sense of wonder and pride that would not be out of place in a seventeenth century workshop fashioning matchlock weapons.

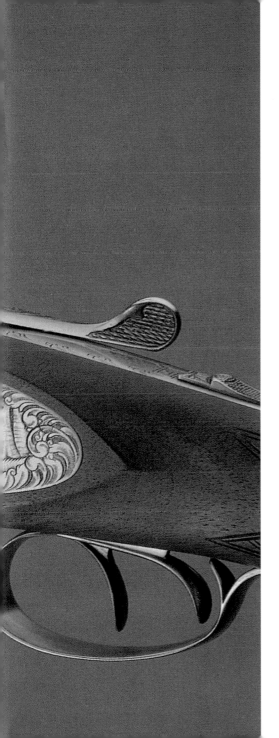

Rifles and Small Arms Through the Ages

Rifles and Small Arms Through the Ages

In the past, the invention of gunpowder has been ascribed to varied sources such as the Chinese, the Greeks, the Arabs, and the Hindus, but none of these claims withstand critical testing.

The first small arms

The first undisputed records of the existence of gunpowder occur in the writings of Roger Bacon, a Franciscan Friar of Ilchester. From that time on, records became more numerous and gunpowder, though expensive, became more common.

But the question of the purpose that gunpowder had is often debated. Bacon refers to it being wrapped in parchment and ignited to give a "blinding flash and stunning noise." How, and when, and by whom the ability to use it to propel a missile was discovered, is not known with any certainty. For years the legend of

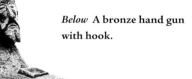

Below **A bronze hand gun with hook.**

Black Berthold, the mysterious monk of Freiburg, held sway; that one day he was preparing gunpowder in an apothecary's mortar when the mixture ignited and blew the pestle from the mortar.

According to this story, the monk then deduced the use of gunpowder in a closed vessel, and invented the gun. Unfortunately, no two authorities seem to have agreed on when Berthold performed this vital experiment. Recent researchers have suggested that Berthold never existed at all.

The earliest incontestable record of a firearm is the famous Millimete Cannon, so called from being depicted in a 1326 manuscript by Walter de Millimete of England. In the same year there is reference in the records of Florence to the provision of guns. It would thus seem that by 1326 the cannon was

Right **An early siege. Soldiers with hand guns, accompanied by archers and artillery.**

MAKING GUNPOWDER

Gunpowder is an intimate mixture of saltpeter, charcoal, and sulfur: the earliest formula, that of Roger Bacon, gives the proportions as 7:5:5, or 41% saltpeter, 29.5% charcoal, and 29.5% sulfur. This gradually changed, the percentage of saltpeter increasing, until by the end of the eighteenth century it had reached its final form: 75% saltpeter, 15% charcoal, and 10% sulfur. The earliest powder was called "serpentine." This had certain defects: packed tightly in a gun chamber it was difficult to ignite and slow to burn, and in storage had a distinct tendency to separate out its constituent parts.

During the fifteenth century the French invented "corned" powder, in which the three substances were mixed together in the wet state (which was safer than dry mixing). The resulting paste dried. This was then crumbled and passed through strainers to produce granular powder. Such powder was more efficient in the gun, since the interstices between the grains allowed faster ignition and combustion, and since each grain was a solid compound the individual substances could not separate out. Early woodcuts shown below demonstrate various stages in the making of powder.

known across Europe and, by inference, must have been known for some time to allow such distribution to take place. The principal difficulty in identifying the early use of firearms is the haphazard, and somewhat ambiguous use of the word "artillery."

In the 1350s, we begin to see references to *gunnis cum telar* — guns with handles — marking the emergence of the personal firearm.

Top **A cast barrel attached to the remains of its stock by an iron strap, tentatively dated as early fifteenth century.**

Above **Swiss hand gun of the fourteenth century, one fitted with a recoil hook to become a hakenbuchse.**

In the normal course of events we might reasonably expect that a new device would begin small and become larger as experience was gained, but with firearms, this natural order of things is reversed. The first firearms were cannons, and from this beginning design moved in two directions, upward to make bigger and more powerful cannons, and downward to make "hand gonnes."

In general, hand guns appear to have first consisted of a wooden stave to which a cast bronze or iron barrel was fixed by iron bands. In some cases the barrel appears to have been cast as an open-ended tube, a plug being driven into the rear end in order to seal it. A vent, or touch-hole, was drilled through the metal at the rear end of the bore.

To fire, the hand gun was charged with a quantity of powder and a ball or a handful of stones or small shot. Powder was then sprinkled in the vent, and the weapon grasped by its stave, tucking the stave under the arm. A hot iron was then applied to the vent to ignite the priming powder, and this flashed down the vent and into the chamber to ignite the propelling charge of powder and thus discharge the shot. The gun would recoil due to the force of the explosion and the discharge of the shot, and some hand guns have been found with the end of the staff formed into a knob or ball, which might have been rested on the ground to absorb some of the recoil thrust.

A reliable system appeared later when a hook or spur was cast beneath the barrel or attached to the staff. This could then be hooked over a parapet or wagon-body so that the shock was taken by something more resistant than the man holding the gun. These pieces became known as *hakenbuchse* (meaning "hook" in Old German), and later as *arquebus*.

From hackbutt to wheel-lock

By the early part of the fifteenth century the hand gun began to change its form. The large-caliber weapons were difficult to fire, while the serpentine matchlock made control slightly easier. The match had been moved to the side of the weapon, making it feasible to take aim across the top of the barrel. But the long stock or tiller, tucked under the arm, made this impossible.

The hand gun with the hook beneath the barrel now became the *hagbut* or *hackbut*. In the past this has

frequently been confused with the *arquebus*, but the distinction between hackbut and arquebus is apparent from a 1527 French document which records the pay of *arquebusiers* and *hacbuttiers*, and notes that the latter were paid ten times as much as the former. But as the *arquebus* was improved, it overtook the *hackbut*, and by the latter half of the sixteenth century, the *hackbut* was fast disappearing.

Below **Two ball-butted pistols of characteristic German pattern, the stocks of both inlaid with engraved staghorn.**

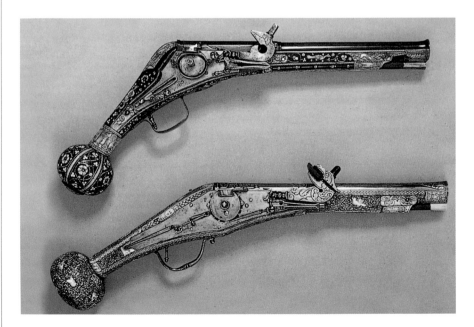

Above A German wheel-lock carbine dating from about 1620. The squared end of the wheel axle, upon which the spanner fits, can be seen, the wheel being concealed within the lock casing. The cock, holding the pyrites, is folded forward in the safe position and the pan cover is closed.

As the *hackbut* became lighter, the need for the hook was reduced, since a man could support the recoil. The bore of the gun decreased, as did the size of the bullet and powder charge: the barrel was made lighter, longer, and more slender, giving better direction to the ball. All that remained was to make the gun controllable, and this was achieved by developing the first full stock, generally called the Lansknecht Stock, after the German mercenaries who devised it. It consisted of a length of wood with a step in it so that the rear end of the barrel butted against the step while the whole barrel was supported by the wood, and retained in place by iron straps. The rear end was shaped roughly to fit against the man's shoulder, and the usual type of serpentine lock was retained.

Soon craftsmen began carving the butt and stock, decorating it, and, at the same time, developing the serpentine lock into a more compact and reliable form. This improvement to the hand gun led to the *arquebus*.

To achieve greater accuracy, rudimentary sights became more common. As early as 1450 there are examples of guns fitted with a simple blade foresight and an upright block with a notch for a rearsight. By 1500 a rearsight made by fixing two metal plates parallel to the barrel and filling the space between them with lead, and then filing a groove in the lead, was in use. The earliest guns were so inaccurate that they could dispense with sights, but as the accuracy improved, the desire to hit the target led to acceptance of sighting devices.

Matchlock and wheel-lock
The first attempt at mechanically firing a hand gun was with the serpentine. To make this idea effective it was necessary to enlarge the mouth of the touch-hole into a pan, in which powder could be

Above An English musket rest of about 1630, the wooden shaft inlaid with mother-of-pearl and engraved staghorn. Below it a French matchlock of about 1575, the walnut stock inlaid with engraved and stained staghorn.

sprinkled, thus giving a larger ignition area and decreasing the need for an accurate and therefore difficult connection with the match.

The next step was to make the serpentine less cumbersome, and thus the snapping matchlock evolved. In this system the burning match was held at the tip of a curved arm which was hinged to the stock of the weapon. A short lever bore against this arm, keeping it away from the touch-hole, and a rod, through the stock, was attached to this lever so that pressure on the rod by the firer's thumb or finger would disengage the lever and allow the curved arm to fall by its own weight and so bring the match into contact with the powder.

The match referred to was a length of tow, twisted from hemp, flax, or cotton, and then soaked in a strong solution of saltpeter and allowed to dry. When ignited it burned at about one inch per minute, and a suitable length could be clamped into the end of the curved arm and ignited before battle commenced. An even slower rate of burning could be achieved by varying the stretch of the saltpeter solution.

The snapping matchlock was first replaced by a primitive trigger mechanism, derived from that used on the crossbow, and then by a neater trigger and sear mechanism concealed within a lock mechanism inserted into the stock. The curved arm was given a notch into which a metal strut fitted, and a spring to propel it forward. The strut was controlled by the trigger, so that pressure on the trigger removed the strut and allowed the match arm to be driven forward by the spring to make contact with the powder in the touch-hole. In this form the matchlock survived until the latter part of the eighteenth century, largely because of its cheapness and simplicity.

By 1530 the wheel-lock had been invented, introducing the first self-contained ignition system. Although it appears to have originated in Italy, the wheel-lock seems to have attained its greatest perfection in Germany.

The wheel, from which the lock derived its name, had a serrated edge and revolved immediately behind, and partially into, the powder pan leading to the touch-hole and barrel. A short chain was attached to the axle of the wheel and to a powerful leaf spring and the axle had an exposed square end to enable a spanner to turn the wheel backward against the pressure of the spring. When the wheel was turned back far enough, a peg entered a recess in the wheel and was retained there by the trigger mechanism. A "dog" or "cock" — a hinged arm — carried a piece of iron pyrites clamped in its jaw. It was also under spring pressure, and was retained by a catch linked to the trigger. Pressing the trigger released the dog which swung over to strike

the circumference of the wheel, which had also been released and was spinning forward. The serrated edge struck sparks from the pyrites, and the sparks fell into the pan and fired the weapon.

Several methods to achieve this mechanical end were developed over two centuries. A pan cover was soon adopted, keeping the powder dry and in place, linked to either the wheel or cock so that it opened automatically as the sparks were struck. Some mechanisms used gearing to make spinning the wheel easier, or to make it rotate longer, while others used the movement of pulling the cock forward to wind up the wheel spring and perform both actions at once. Less common were locks that used merely a segment of the wheel (the sector lock) or even a flat piece of metal with teeth (the rasp lock).

Below **A richly decorated Italian seventeenth century matchlock gun, with the match cord carried in its holder.**

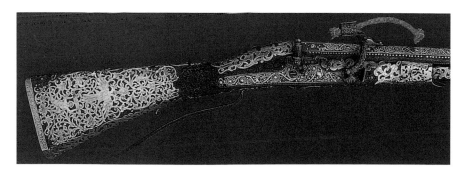

The snaphaunce

In the sixteenth century the sure road to fame and fortune for any weapon designer or manufacturer was to obtain a contract for military supply. Therefore if the wheel-lock was not acceptable to the military, something cheaper and simpler had to be found.

Once again, a precise time and place cannot be provided for the snaphaunce, though every indication points to Germany as its birthplace. The basic mechanism was that of a spring-loaded arm, the cock, which

carried a shaped piece of flint in jaws at its outer end. The pan was now covered by a steel "frizzen," an arm which was hinged ahead of the pan and which had an upturned and concave face at its free end. The relative positions of cock and frizzen were so arranged that when the cock fell forward under the impetus of its spring, the flint was driven hard across the curved face of the frizzen in order to strike sparks. At the same time, the curved face of the frizzen and its pivot point led to a complex

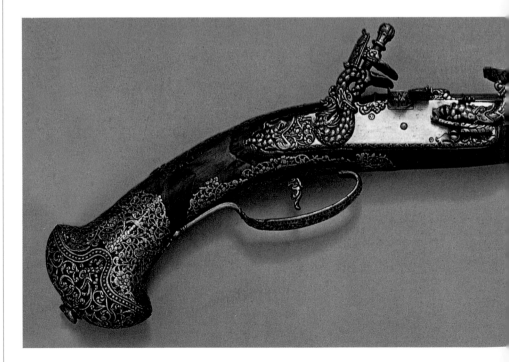

interplay of forces in which the impact of the cock caused the frizzen arm to fly up so to allow the struck sparks to pass into the pan and ignite the priming.

These locks were known as "snaphaunce" locks; the origin of the term is in some doubt. Some writers claim that it comes from the Dutch

snap Haens, meaning "hen thief," ascribing this derivation to the early use of the lock by poachers. More likely is the derivation from German: *Schnapphahn* or "snapping hammer," which seems more feasible if the German origin of the lock is accepted.

Irrespective of its origin, the snaphaunce soon spread across Europe and there, certain local preferences and peculiarities emerged. The Swedish or Baltic version, for example, was characterized by an extremely long arm and jaw to the

Below **A snaphaunce holster-pistol, the walnut stock inlaid with mounts of pierced iron, the barrels signed "Lazarino Cominazzo"; Brescia, about 1650.**

cock, which appears to have been derived from matchlock design. The Spanish lock, sometimes called the "miquelet" lock, had the frizzen shaped to form a pan cover, so that the powder was not exposed until the actual moment of ignition. With all snaphaunces, the cock was drawn back with the thumb against spring pressure; the lower end of the cock was then rested on a cross bolt, or sear, and actuated by the trigger so

that pulling the trigger withdrew the sear and allowed the cock to fall. In the Spanish lock there was a second sear which moved out beneath the toe of the cock as it was pulled back almost as soon as it began to move, and prevented fire being struck if the

Below **A pair of snaphaunce pistols with mounts of chiseled iron by Giuseppe Guardiani of Anghiari. Italian, late eighteenth century.**

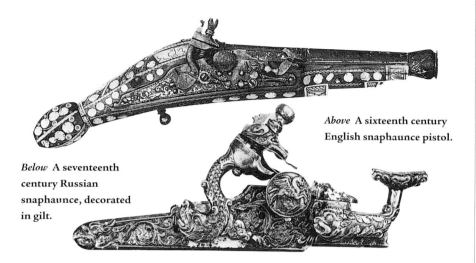

Above **A sixteenth century English snaphaunce pistol.**

Below **A seventeenth century Russian snaphaunce, decorated in gilt.**

cock accidentally slipped during the cocking movement. Once this half cock sear was under the cock, the weapon could be safely carried; the pan cover could be operated; and the trigger could not be pulled, since the trigger sear was not in play. Without the half-cock feature the pan could not be opened if the cock were left forward, but when the weapon was cocked and then loaded, it could only be carried in a most careful fashion for fear of accidental discharge. The Spanish lock's half-cock sear was withdrawn from its blocking position by cam action when the cock was drawn to full-cock position.

The Dutch snaphaunce lock separated the frizzen and pan cover into two distinct components, and linked the sliding pan cover to the cock by a simple lever. Thus as the cock fell, the pan cover was thrust open in time to receive the sparks. To carry the gun safely, the frizzen could be thrown up, out of the path of the cock, without exposing the priming. The English Lock used a combined frizzen and pan cover and took its nickname from the sear mechanism in which the cock was a notch in its lower edge into which a dog-catch snapped by spring power as the cock was pulled back. This dog was withdrawn by the action of the trigger.

Although the snaphaunce lock became the standard method of ignition, it was also incorporated into highly ornamental weapons, carefully made for wealthy patrons.

The simpler flintlock

People had used flint to strike sparks for thousands of years. It was therefore not surprising that this system should be applied to firearms — the only problem lay in how to achieve it. The flintlock appeared in the sixteenth century, though the exact origin of its birthplace is in some doubt.

The first was probably the Spanish lock or *miquelet*, of which there is record as early as 1547. It was probably developed by Simon Marquette, the son of an Italian gun maker who had settled in Spain. It consisted of a cock with jaws, which

gripped a piece of flint, and a frizzen, an angled steel plate which covered the priming pan and also intercepted the fall of the spring-driven cock when the trigger was pulled. After the weapon was loaded with powder and ball, the cock was pulled back until a cross-bolt, or sear, moved across the lock frame to hold it back. The frizzen was then hinged forward to

Below **A top-quality flintlock pistol by London maker William Parker, procuded about 1820. Such items may be acquired from dealers and auction houses, although not always in the fine condition as the one shown here.**

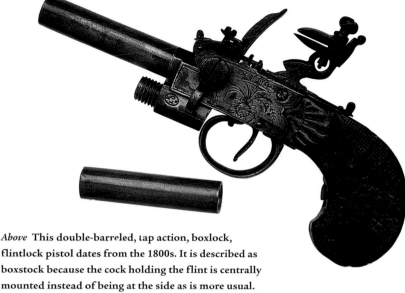

Above This double-barreled, tap action, boxlock, flintlock pistol dates from the 1800s. It is described as boxstock because the cock holding the flint is centrally mounted instead of being at the side as is more usual. Tap action refers to the selection of the barrel to be fired, which is done by means of the ring mounted on the side.

expose the pan, powder was sprinkled into the pan, and the frizzen pulled back to cover the pan and hold the powder in place. On pulling the trigger forward the flint struck the flat rear face of the frizzen. This struck sparks from the flint, and the impact knocked the frizzen forward, exposing the powder in the pan to the falling sparks.

At much the same time as the *miquelet*, the Dutch *snaphaunce* lock appeared. This used the same elements as the Spanish lock, but was different in some important respects. For example, the main spring pulled the cock rather than pushing it, and the frizzen acted only to strike sparks.

The pan cover was a separate, sliding component with a rod to link it to the cock, so that as the cock moved forward, it pushed the pan cover open. Another significant difference was that the Spanish lock carried its spring on the outside, where it could be easily repaired, whereas the Dutch lock carried it inside, where it was better protected against damage.

Once these two locks had been introduced, variations followed. The English dog-lock appears to have been derived from the Dutch lock, and takes its name from the addition of a "dog," or small hook, on the side of the lock frame behind the cock. On pulling back the cock, this hook

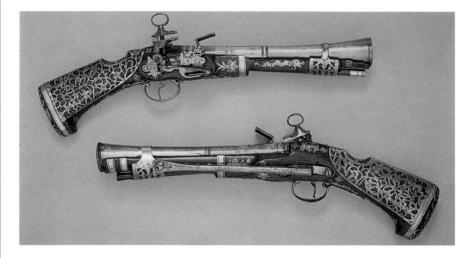

Above **Two Spanish miquelet-lock blunderbusses, 1690.**

snapped into a recess in the cock to hold it at the half-cock position, from which it could not be fired by using the trigger. The only way to fire was to pull back the cock to the full-cock position and thumb the dog out of the way while pulling the trigger. The English adopted the Spanish system of making the frizzen and pan cover in one piece, but kept the Dutch method of concealing the main spring inside the lock. The Swedish lock used a long and slender cock, which gave the lock a very distinct appearance. The separate frizzen and concealed spring of the Dutch lock were used, but the pan cover was not connected to the cock, and had to be opened before pulling the trigger.

After studying these variations, the French perfected the mechanism into the final flintlock design, the French lock. Their first attempt resembled the Dutch design, but without the interconnected pan cover. Their principal innovation was the "tumbler", a shaped cam inside the lock on the rotating shaft which carried the cock. The tumbler had notches which engaged with the trigger in order to enable full and half-cock positions, and also a notch for the mainspring to provide the driving force for the cock.

This model was soon superseded by the perfected French model, which eventually became the accepted standard.

Operating the flintlock

The flintlock's powder and shot could be loaded before or after priming the pan, although standard military practice was to prime the pan before loading the barrel. In order to prime, the cock was drawn back, usually to the half-cock position, the frizzen opened, and fine powder sprinkled into the pan from a powder flask. The frizzen was then snapped shut, and the cock drawn back to the full-cock position. On the order "Present!" the weapon was raised and pointed at the target; on "Fire!" the trigger was pulled, releasing the cock to fly forward and strike the frizzen. This generated sparks, and the blow of the cock threw the frizzen forward, exposing the powder in the pan to the failing sparks, and so igniting the charge in the barrel.

Right A brass-barreled flintlock holster pistol from 1800 or later. The lock is marked "London Warranted", which suggests that it was a trade gun made for sale or barter with British colonies or other countries. The standard of workmanship is barely competent, and such pieces are not greatly valued and may be acquired from specialist dealers at reasonable prices. Similar items were still being made in Belgium until the late nineteenth century.

The percussion principle

The flintlock's action could be distinguished as three separate events: first the fall of the cock and striking of sparks; second the ignition of the priming; and third the explosion of the cartridge and ejection of the bullet. In military application, this led to long and intensive training of recruits, since the normal reaction was to flinch as the priming fired and thus disturb aim before the cartridge exploded.

In the sporting application, the snap of the flint and the flash of the priming often alerted the game, which moved with lightning reaction, and was no longer there when the bullet or shot arrived. Hunters became adept at forecasting how far and in which direction the game would spring or fly, and aimed-off accordingly, which turned hunting into a game of chance.

Among the hunters who suffered was the Reverend Alexander Forsyth of Belhelvie, Aberdeenshire, who began to apply his mind to the problem of making a weapon capable of instantaneous discharge. In 1800, Edward Howard of the Royal Society discovered fulminate of mercury, a sensitive substance which, when struck, detonated violently: doubtless Forsyth had heard of this, and he began his own experiments. In 1807 he patented a system of ignition which relied on a detonating powder which was composed largely of potassium chlorate.

In Forsyth's lock, the frizzen and pan were replaced by a small

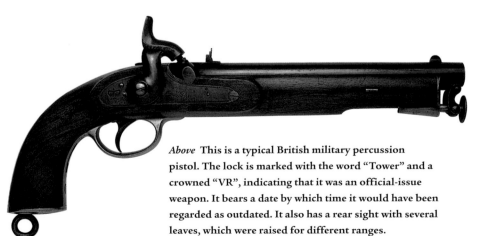

Above This is a typical British military percussion pistol. The lock is marked with the word "Tower" and a crowned "VR", indicating that it was an official-issue weapon. It bears a date by which time it would have been regarded as outdated. It also has a rear sight with several leaves, which were raised for different ranges.

Above **A pair of pocket pistols made in 1815 by Alexander Forsyth and Company, complete with accessories. These are fitted with Forsyth's patented sliding primers. In front of the hammer is a small box containing percussion powder. As the hammer is drawn back to cock the pistol, the box slides back and deposits a quantity of the powder into the pan.**

revolving magazine resembling a flask — it became known as the "scent bottle lock" from its shape — which contained a supply of detonating powder. This magazine pivoted around an axis which was bored through the side of the gun barrel, to provide a vent into the chamber. The flint-carrying cock was replaced by a simple hammer. The gun was loaded with powder and shot in the usual way, and then the magazine was revolved a half-turn about its axis. This brought the powder receptacle above the vent, and a small measure of detonating powder dropped down and charged the vent. The magazine was then turned back half a turn, which took the magazine section down to the blind side of the vent, and positioned a loosely held pin above the powder in the vent.

On pulling the trigger the hammer fell, striking the pin which was driven down into the vent, crushed the powder, and exploded it. The resulting flame ran down the vent and fired the gunpowder charge.

Once Forsyth had shown the way, practical gunsmiths were quick to make improvements. Forsyth and James Purdey, a prominent gunsmith, changed the scent bottle lock to a similar sliding pattern, which was linked to the hammer. As the hammer was cocked, the magazine slid forward, bringing a firing pin into position to be struck by the hammer. Similar locks were produced by

gunsmiths on the continent, but the use of loose detonating powder had its drawbacks, and alternative systems of priming soon appeared.

One early idea was to make small pills of powder and coat them with varnish or gum. These were placed in the vent and struck by the hammer. Such a system came from contemporary apothecary's practice,

Below **A four-barreled, all-steel, turnover pistol was originally made as a flintlock in Belgium in 1750. It was later converted into percussion by modifying the hammers and screwing nipples into the vents.**

as did an alternative system of sealing pinches of powder between two disks of paper. This alternative system has survived to this day in the caps used by children in toy guns.

Another ingenious system placed the powder at the closed end of a small copper tube. The open end was thrust into the vent, and the hammer fell in order to crush the closed end, firing the powder and sending the flash into the gun vent.

All these systems had some degree of success, but the one which eventually superseded all others was the most simple, that of the percussion cap. This appears to have been developed simultaneously by several inventors between 1818 and 1823. After some false starts, the percussion cap settled down to a very simple pattern — that of a top hat of copper with a small coating of detonating powder inside the crown, secured there by a coat of varnish which also served to waterproof it. The gun vent now ended in an upturned nipple with a central hole

upon which the cap was placed, open end down. The hammer fell, crushing the cap against the edges of the nipple, and thus fired the detonating powder in order to send a powerful flash down the vent. A slight defect of the early caps was that, due to weak copper and strong powder, the caps frequently split and fragments flew off and endangered the firer. This was countered by making the hammer face hollow, so that at the moment of ignition the cap was entirely surrounded by steel. Another system adopted to guard against the disintegrating cap was to place the nipple below the breech, and arrange the hammer to strike upward so that the body of the gun was between the cap and the firer's face. These under-hammer guns enjoyed some popularity, and actually appeared as military weapons in Scandinavia.

Above Right **The brass trigger guard bears the incription "Dismounted Horse Patrol," which identifies the pistol as an example of early London Police Pistol. In the early nineteenth century, this strangely named unit patrolled the streets of London from their station in Bow Street.**

Breech-loading firearms

The Industrial Revolution brought about many changes, but one of the least appreciated (or so it seems) was that it became respectable to be an engineer. The nineteenth century thus saw the engineer reach a status he had never enjoyed before, nor has done since. Consequently, many intelligent and ingenious minds, which otherwise might not have contemplated mechanical problems, suddenly discovered innumerable technical problems waiting to be solved, with the added stimulus of the sizable fortune to be earned for the best solution. Many of these minds began studying firearms, and how they could be improved.

Below **An English breech-loader by Rowland, 1720.**

Most people agreed that one way to improve firearms would be to load them from the breech end, and do away with the prolonged performance with powder, ball, and ramrod. There was nothing new in this idea, since breech-loading firearms had been attempted right from the earliest days, particularly with cannon. But in those early days, there was little real understanding of what went on inside the gun when it fired, or of the type and magnitude of the pressures and temperatures involved. Moreover, the ability to machine metal to fine limits on a production basis simply did not exist. It was one thing to spend months carefully hand-fitting a pistol for sale at a high price to a noble patron, but a totally different matter to attempt to duplicate it on a scale suitable to equipping an army.

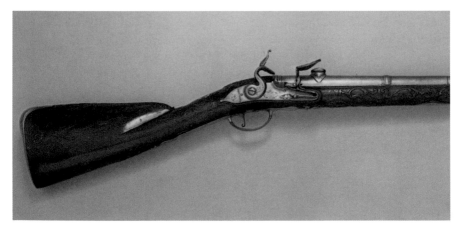

Above A flintlock pistol with turn-off
barrel, breech-loading, and self-priming
repeating action according to the
Lorenzoni design. The ball and powder are
taken from the magazines in the butt

Some of the earliest known breech-
loading small arms are two carbines
and two shield pistols made for
Henry VIII. The carbines used a trapdoor at the rear of the barrel which
could be lifted to insert an iron tube
charged with powder and ball.
Ignition was sparked by wheel-lock
through a vent incorporated in the
tube. The shield pistols used a similar
loading system but were matchlocks
— and that itself is remarkable,
for only one other specimen of a
matchlock pistol is known. However,
in spite of excellent workmanship
for their time, the sealing of the
breeches of these weapons left a lot
to be desired.

The next attempt at breech-
loading to amount to anything was
an invention by de la Chaumette, a
Frenchman, who in 1704 drilled a
large vertical hole through the rear
end of a musket barrel, cut a thread
on it, and then closed the hole by a
screwed plug inserted from below.
The trigger guard formed a handle
for the plug, and a few turns were
sufficient to lower the top of the
plug so that powder and ball could
be inserted into the breech. The plug
was then screwed up, and the gun
was fired by the usual flintlock
mechanism. Chaumette seems to have
had relatively little success with the
design, though some sporting guns
were made according to this design.
The design then lay more or less
neglected until revived and improved
by Patrick Ferguson, a Scottish
soldier, in the 1770s. Ferguson made
the breech plug with a quick thread,
so that a half-turn was enough to
open the breech for loading. He also
made the breech section of the plug
with a smooth surface, so that

fouling could not jam the action. He then placed a greater thickness of metal below the breech to take the screw thread, so that the plug could be lowered below the chamber level to facilitate cleaning the bore.

In 1776 Ferguson demonstrated his rifle in front of the Master General of the Ordinance. On a wet and windy day at Woolwich Marshes he fired his new gun at a steady rate of four or five shots a minute, and then capped this by walking towards the target, loading, and firing as he went. As a result, one hundred Ferguson Rifles were ordered to be made, a special Light Company of 100 men was raised and, commanded by Ferguson and armed with the rifles, was sent to America. But the first major engagement of the Ferguson rifle was destined to be its last, though from no fault of the rifle's design. Ferguson and his light

company were part of a diversionary attack at Brandywine Creek on 11 September 1777. They did manage to acquit themselves with distinction, until Ferguson was wounded by an American bullet.

Without its motivating leader, the Light Company was dispersed and the hundred rifles disappeared. Ferguson recovered from his wound, but before he could make a start in reforming the Light Company, he was killed at the Battle of King's Mountain, and the Ferguson rifle was never revived. The greatest mystery of all is what happened to his rifles — only one or two of the original hundred are known to exist today, though others made by gunsmiths for the Honorable East India Company and for private owners, have survived.

The first nation to adopt a breech-loader as standard was the United States, when it began issuing the Hall

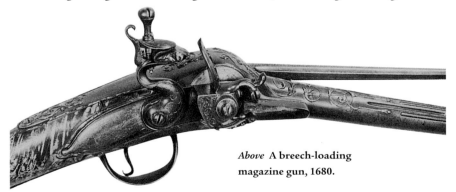

Above **A breech-loading magazine gun, 1680.**

Left A four-barreled Sharps pistol. The hammer is pulled back for each shot and the firing pin assembly rotates to bring it in line with an unfired barrel.

Carbine in 1819. This had the rear section of the barrel (the chamber) separated from the rest, and hinged at the rear so that it could be tipped up and loaded. Ignition was by percussion, and the chamber section also carried the hammer and nipple so that the loaded chamber could be withdrawn from the rifle and carried in the pocket to serve as an emergency pistol. Another innovative feature of the Hall carbine was that it was manufactured by machinery on an assembly-line principle, and the parts were therefore interchangeable. It was far from perfect, for the joint between chamber and barrel soon began to leak due to the erosive effect of the hot gases, but it did remain in service for almost fifty years.

It was the self-contained cartridge (a cartridge which held powder) bullet and means of ignition which provided the complete answer to the breech-loading puzzle. It was not until this apparently obvious point was appreciated by Johannes Pauly of Switzerland, that progress began to be made.

Although Pauly's guns were greeted with acclaim by such figures as Napoleon and the Czar of Russia, they failed to achieve commercial success, and in 1814 he moved to London, where he died three years later.

The revolver

Throughout the history of firearms there were periodic attempts to devise weapons which could be loaded with several charges and bullets, and then discharged repeatedly without having to reload between shots.

The Ducksfoot pistol, with five or six splayed-out barrels was one example. Another famous weapon was Nock's Volley Gun, a seven-barreled short musket produced for the Royal Navy in the 1780s. In the seventeenth century came the idea of having one fixed barrel, but placing a cylinder containing a number of loaded chambers behind it, and then discharging them one at a time through the barrel. The drawback here was the difficulty of arranging ignition — either a single pan and lock served each chamber in turn and had to be reprimed for each shot, or each chamber had its own loaded pan and frizzen — neither system was entirely satisfactory. Towards the end of the eighteenth century the Pepperbox pistol became popular; this used a revolving cluster of barrels, and was fired by a flintlock. Each barrel was hand-turned into alignment with the lock.

In 1818 Captain Artemus Wheeler of Concord, Massachusetts, obtained a patent for a gun that discharged seven or more times. This might be said to mark the birth of the revolver as we know it today. Wheeler's design was actually for a carbine or short musket, with a hand-revolved cylinder

Below **Collier's second model of about 1820 with improvements, including an external cock and fluted cylinder.**

Above This early percussion revolver is one of a type and usually described as transitional because it falls between the pepperbox and true percussion revolver. This example was possibly made by the British maker Brazier. Examples of this kind of revolver are not uncommon.

and flint ignition. It was examined by the United States Navy in 1821, but was turned down. In the meantime, Wheeler's assistant, Elisha Collier, came to England and secured a patent for a firearm that combined a single barrel with several chambers to obtain a succession of discharges from one loading. Collier never denied that his inspiration came from Wheeler, but he incorporated some important features which lifted the design far beyond those which had preceded it. The most innovative feature was the provision of a spring to revolve the cylinder when the hammer was cocked. Another important feature was that the cylinder moved forward under spring pressure, so that the rear end of the barrel entered into the mouth of the cylinder to form a close joint which

prevented the escape of flame and gas on firing. Other mechanical linkages were provided in order to lock the cylinder in place against the recoil force.

Altogether the Collier pistol was a considerable advance, and although it did fail to be adopted as a military weapon, the idea had some commercial success. Several English gunsmiths obtained licenses from Collier to manufacture revolving pistols, shotguns, and rifles according to his patent.

The period of the Collier revolver spanned the time during which the percussion cap came into use, and his designs were changed accordingly in order to use this system of ignition, which proved to be a far less involved matter than his original flintlock system. The percussion cap also revitalized the pepperbox revolver, and the bar-hammer pepperbox (so called from the long hammer which stretched across the top of the pistol in order to reach the nipples on each barrel) became popular in England and America.

Below **A Colt Single Action Army Revolver, which has been in production for longer than almost any other hand gun. Introduced in 1873, it is still made today. This example is unusual as the caliber is .357in Magnum, and only a comparatively small number of this type of revolver were manufactured.**

The English designs were particularly important since they introduced trigger mechanisms which automatically rotated the barrel cluster, locked it in place, and cocked and released the hammer all in one pull of the trigger. This was called the self-cocking mechanism.

In spite of the efficiency of these arms, there was no great market for them. The London Proof House returns for the 1830–1850 period show that the average number of revolving arms submitted for proof (as they had to be before sale) was no more than about 300 per year.

Above **A Dragoon 3rd Model percussion revolver with Holster, 1853/4. This weapon belonged to Captain Francis T. Bryan of the United States Army and saw service on the American frontier. A heavy weapon, it fired a bullet of .44in caliber. The cylinder was engraved with a scene of a fight with American Indians. All of Colt's early revolvers were single action, which means that the hammer had to be pulled back before the trigger could be pressed to fire the weapon.**

The revolver did not make a great appeal to the public until 1851, when the Great Exhibition was held in London and Samuel Colt displayed his wares to the public.

After going into liquidation with his first revolver venture, Colt was given a second chance by the advent of the Mexican War of 1847, and from then on, aided by the 1849 Gold Rush, his company prospered. In 1851 his exhibits in London attracted enormous interest, which he carefully fostered by a variety of astute publicity stunts, and suddenly the western world began to clamor for revolvers.

Colt's revolvers followed the open frame pattern whereby the butt frame carried the hammer and cylinder, and the barrel was affixed to the front of the frame by a removable key. Thus there was no connection between the barrel and the upper portion of the frame, and the top surface of the cylinder was exposed. By knocking out the key, the barrel could be removed, followed by the cylinder, for cleaning. After this the cylinder could be loaded with powder and ball or with prepared paper cartridges, caps placed on the nipples, and the gun reassembled. To simplify reloading, Colt developed a lever-rammer which lay beneath the barrel and could be unclipped to allow the chambers to be reloaded without having to dismantle the weapon completely.

At the 1851 Exhibition, Colt's only serious competitor was Robert Adams of London. Adams had developed the solid frame revolver in which the butt frame and barrel were forged as a single piece of metal, and the rectangle into which the cylinder was fitted was left in the frame. This resulted in a much stronger form of construction. Adams also used a different firing mechanism to that of Colt. The Colt was a single action pistol in which the hammer had to be manually cocked for each shot, being released by pressure on the trigger. The Adams was a self-cocking pistol in which pulling the trigger lifted and dropped the hammer. Both systems

have their advantages, however the single action was better for accuracy since the relatively light pull needed to release the cocked hammer was unlikely to upset the aim. The self-cocking lock demanded a much greater effort to pull through on the trigger, and this invariably caused the pistol to waver off its aim. On the other hand, for rapid fire in action, the self-cocking lock was preferred since the firer merely had to keep pulling on the trigger.

With the advent of metallic cartridges, the revolver designers now had to devise methods of loading and unloading at the rear of the cylinder. This led to a plethora of patented contraptions. Eventually three systems outlived the rest: gate loading, in which the cartridges were inserted one at a time into the chambers through a gate or trap at the side of the breech; the hinged frame, in which the barrel and

Above The English gunsmith Robert Adams loading the revolver of HRH the Prince Consort.

cylinder swung away from the frame to expose the rear face of the cylinder; and the side-opening solid frame revolver in which the cylinder was carried on a crane arm and could be swung out to lie alongside the frame for loading. Extraction of the empty cases was achieved in the first case by a rod beneath the barrel which, thrust backward, pushed the spent cases through the gate one by one. In the other two cases a plate was arranged in the center of the cylinder to move outward, catching beneath the cartridge case rims, and thus ejecting them.

Except for aberrant forms such as the Webley-Fosbery automatic revolver, the Landstadt, and the Dardick revolvers, the basic pattern for revolvers was settled by the early 1890s, and development since then has largely been in matters of detail or improved systems of manufacture.

The rifle

The earliest known rifled arm is a matchlock hunting rifle which was owned by the Emperor Maximilian in 1500. Many hypotheses have been advanced to account for the development of rifling, but none have ever been confirmed.

But even if the theory was absent, practical results provided enough evidence, and from the sixteenth century onward, rifled arms were made. At first, rifles were not made in great numbers, since rifling was a long, difficult, and hence costly process. Because of the cost, rifles were originally the property of wealthy hunters and sportsmen. Moreover, the owners had to take pains with their ammunition, casting their own bullets very precisely to ensure that they would fit the rifling grooves correctly, for a bullet which was too loose a fit was of little or no use. This, of course, led to problems after a few shots had been fired — the fouling set up by the residue from the burned gunpowder charge made it harder and harder to force the ball down the barrel, and the bullet generally had to be started in the muzzle by a wooden mallet. Eventually, the shooter had no alternative but to stop firing and thoroughly clean the barrel before he could continue.

Very soon it was found that a simpler way was to "patch" the bullet, or to enclose it in a cloth or thin leather wad which had been greased.

Above A rifle of Ferguson pattern. This shows the screwed breech plug in its open position, achieved by a turn of the combined lever and trigger-guard. Ignition was by the normal flintlock.

Right **Lieutenant Colonel Patrick Ferguson began designing his rifle in 1774. He demonstrated it before officers at Woolwich, which resulted in orders for 100 rifles. Ferguson supervised manufacture, trained a company of men in the use of the rifle, and sailed for America in 1777.**

The ball used with this system was of smaller caliber than the barrel, and thus ball and patch could be easily rammed down. On firing, the patch would set up and fill the rifling grooves behind the bullet, grip the ball, impart the desired spin, and then fall clear as it left the muzzle. This also helped to reduce the fouling, since the grease left in the bore softened the powder residue, and the wad swept the grooves clean with each shot.

In spite of the extra expense involved in rifling a weapon, it was soon appreciated that in the hands of trained men, a few rifles could be most effective in battle. Rifles therefore began to appear in military service in the seventeenth century.

Christian IV of Denmark is generally credited with being the first to put the rifle into military service, but he was soon followed by others. In some armies the would-be rifleman was required to provide his own rifle on the assumption that he would probably produce a better weapon than the military could afford, and also that he would already be familiar with it, and thus require little or no further training.

Swiss, German, and Bohemian gunsmiths who immigrated to the New World set up in business and largely concentrated on making hunting rifles. These were, at first, heavy weapons with seven-grooved rifling in large caliber barrels — calibers of .5 to .7in weren't unusual. Such weapons had performed well in European hunting, but conditions in America were somewhat different as a hunting trip was not an afternoon's walk in the woods, but a protracted and strenuous expedition, and

therefore hunters wanted lighter rifles. Hunters further argued that a smaller caliber would kill game just as well and economize on lead. And so the American rifle evolved: a thinner and longer barrel of about .45in caliber with a maple-wood stock and unique patch box incorporated in the butt for spare flints and bullet patches.

The majority of gunsmiths specializing in these weapons settled in Pennsylvania, and the rifle is thus now properly known as the Pennsylvania Rifle. However, today they are often, and incorrectly, called "Kentucky rifles" due to a popular ballad from the War of 1812 which sang of Andrew Jackson's "Kentucky Mountain Men" and their rifles at the Battle of New Orleans.

The principal drawback with the rifle as a military weapon was the

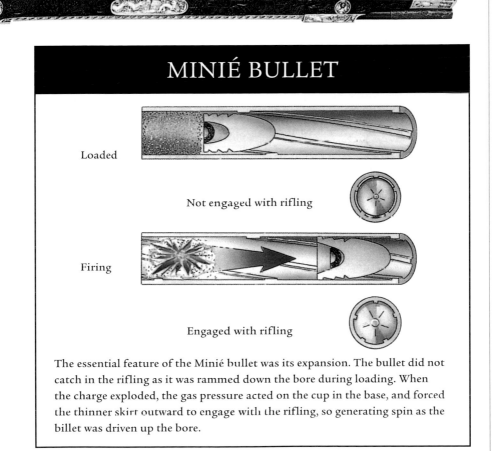

MINIÉ BULLET

Loaded

Not engaged with rifling

Firing

Engaged with rifling

The essential feature of the Minié bullet was its expansion. The bullet did not catch in the rifling as it was rammed down the bore during loading. When the charge exploded, the gas pressure acted on the cup in the base, and forced the thinner skirt outward to engage with the rifling, so generating spin as the billet was driven up the bore.

slowness of loading, even with prepared cartridges. The patch had to be put across the muzzle, and the ball started truly down the bore, and then rammed. As a result, military riflemen were often accompanied by other soldiers armed with muskets in order to be able to produce some improved firepower in the event of a counterattack against the rifleman. The only answer to this would be to produce a bullet which would be of such small diameter that it would pass easily down the bore during loading, but which would by some means, expand to fit tightly into the rifling grooves.

In the 1840s Thouvenin, a Frenchman, developed a pointed cylindrical bullet which was used in a special gun which carried a pillar in the center of the chamber. The powder was loaded first and occupied the space around the pillar. The bullet was then dropped down the barrel so that its base rested on the tip of the pillar, at which point a few sharp blows with the ramrod deformed the base of the bullet so that it spread out by impact on the pillar, and expanded into the rifling.

This worked, but the deformation of the bullet was rather hit-and-miss, and the pounding of the rammer upset the head shape, resulting in irregular flight. A better solution was to hollow out the base of the

bullet, and allow the explosion of the charge to expand the skirt of the bullet into the rifling. This system was first proposed in 1835 by William Greener, an English gunsmith, but in spite of demonstrations, the idea did not catch on. In 1846 a French officer by the name of Captain Minié developed a pointed bullet with a hollow base. With a small iron cup in the base, the lower edge of the bullet was forced out into the rifling under pressure. The Minié bullet, with various minor improvements, became the standard rifle bullet for the remainder of the muzzle-loading era.

Although the usual form of rifling is the polygroove system in which a number of spiral grooves are cut into the barrel, there have been other ways of spinning the bullet. The Brunswick rifle, adopted in British service in

Above **When the Prussian Army adopted the needle gun, the details were carefully kept secret for many years.**

Above **French troops engaged in a streetfight with the Prussian forces during the Franco-Prussian war of 1870. The Chassepot rifle differed from the needle gun in not driving its firing pin entirely through the cartridge, and in having a more efficient rubber breech seal. The caliber was smaller, giving longer range, but the small bore was easily fouled.**

1835, had only two grooves which were opposite each other and unusually deep. The bullet was a ball with a central raised belt which engaged with the grooves as the bullet was loaded, and imparted the spin as it was ejected. Though the theory of the system was sound, the effect of the raised belt on the bullet's flight made it hard to hit anything at ranges greater than 400 yards.

Another idea, developed in Denmark and promoted in England by Lancaster, was to make the gun's bore oval instead of circular, and then develop it into a twist. An oval bullet was used, and following the twisted bore, developed the necessary spin.

A similar idea was the Whitworth Hexagonal Bore in which the rifle barrel was a twisted hexagon with the bullets shaped to suit.

With the arrival of breech loading, most of the aberrant forms of rifling disappeared. Most of these had been concerned with reducing the problems raised by powder fouling, and once it became practical to clean a rifle by passing a brush completely through the barrel, such problems diminished and simple polygroove rifling became the standard pattern.

Pinfire weapons

All percussion revolvers suffered from the same limitation: muzzle loading. Each chamber had to be filled with powder, a bullet rammed down on top of the powder, and a cap placed on the nipple. Paper cartridges, which held one charge of powder and a lead bullet, were commonly used, but they still had to be torn open. There had been experiments with self-contained cartridges, and some had been very successful, although they had not been taken up for various reasons. The first really practical commercial steps were taken soon after the percussion principle had been adopted. This was the system known as pinfire.

In 1835 the Frenchman Casimir Lefaucheux patented a system that used a metal or cardboard cartridge case with a small hole in the side, through which a short metal pin passed. The tip of the rod rested on some fulminate embedded in the powder charge which was itself contained within the case. If this pin were struck, it pressed down to detonate the fulminate and so produce an explosive flash to ignite the charge. Lefaucheux designed guns with a small slot at the breech so that when the cartridge was inserted, the pin could project through it, ready to be struck by the hammer.

The pinfire system was exhibited at the Great Exhibition in London in 1851. But it seems to have attracted little attention despite the fact it made breech loading comparatively simple. Later, Lefaucheux's son, Eugene, patented a revolver using the

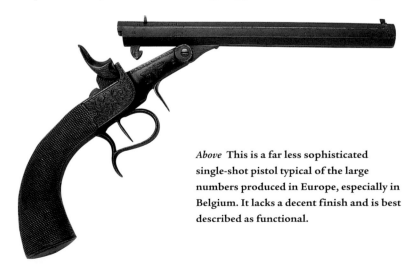

Above **This is a far less sophisticated single-shot pistol typical of the large numbers produced in Europe, especially in Belgium. It lacks a decent finish and is best described as functional.**

Above **This is a particularly fine example of a pinfire revolver made in Liège, Belgium during the nineteenth century.**

pinfire cartridge in France and Britain. Soon his firm was taking orders for military revolvers from several countries, as well as many civilian orders. Britain and the United States showed only limited interest, but on the continent of Europe pinfire revolvers were produced in quantity, and adopted by many countries for their armies. Some saw service during the Civil War, but large numbers were also manufactured for the civilian market and were often sold in cases with a range of accessories. Many revolvers were produced that had, as a safety measure, triggers that folded back to reduce the chances of snagging on clothing or a container.

The ease of loading a metal pinfire cartridge encouraged many European makers to design revolvers with large cylinders holding as many as 12 or 20 shots. A few had even more, although some became so bulky that they

defeated their own purpose. Some makers, such as the French manufacturer Jarre, replaced the cylinder with a flat bar drilled with chambers. Because of its shape, this is usually known as a harmonica gun.

Small revolvers composed of little more than the cylinder and barrel were fitted inside purses and small boxes, and one was combined with a folding knife and knuckle duster to make the Apache pistol. Other small versions were mounted in walking sticks to offer a disguised self-defense weapon.

Most pinfire hand guns were made in Belgium at the manufacturing town of Liége, and they may be easily recognized by the proof mark with the letters ELG, which are stamped into the frame or the cylinder.

The arrival of center-fire

The appearance of the Smith & Wesson revolvers established the basis of the modern hand gun, but one further step was still necessary. Although the rimfire cartridge was a great improvement on previous loading sequences, it did have some limitations. Two men, Colonel Berdan in the United States and Colonel Edward Boxer in Britain, were working toward the next big advances. The outcome of their efforts in the 1860s was the center-fire cartridge. Instead of the fulminate compound being deposited in a thin layer over the inside base of the cartridge case, a percussion cap was fitted into a central hole in the base of the case. The walls and base

of the case could now be of any thickness, since the only part to be hit was the cap. The design of the revolver hammer was also changed so that it had a sharp point rather than the flat bar that had been used on the hammers of rimfire weapons. Detonation was swift and effective, and loading the cartridge was simple thanks to Rollin White's system.

There was still one problem to be resolved, and that was how to insert the cartridges into the chambers of the cylinder. Three basic solutions were devised. On some revolvers,

Below **This .32in revolver with a five-shot cylinder was available in several forms, with square or bird's head butt and with spurred hammers.**

Above **The Mervin Hulbert
revolver is seen opened to
reveal the unusual ejection
system, in which the barrel
was unlocked and then
pulled back together
with the cylinder to extract
the cases.**

such as the Colt Single Action Army, a hinged plate was fitted to the frame just behind the butt end of the cylinder. To load the revolver, this plate or loading gate was flipped sideways to reveal the chambers awaiting the cartridges. The cylinder was rotated to expose each chamber for loading, and the gate was then closed. To extract the empty fired cases, the gate was opened, and some form of spring-loaded rod was fitted, usually below the barrel, which could be pushed back through the chamber to eject the case.

Another solution was to fit the cylinder onto a sideways swinging crane mounted in the frame. Pressing a catch released the pivoted crane so that it could be pushed sideways, taking the cylinder clear of the frame and so allowing easy access to the chambers. Extraction of the cases was effected by a star-shaped plate, located at the center rear of the cylinder, which fitted into a shallow recess of the cylinder. A spring-loaded rod passed through the center of the cylinder and the crane. A push on this rod raised the star, which engaged with the rim of the case and lifted it clear of the cylinder.

The third method was to build the revolver frame in two parts, with the barrel section hinged at the base in front of the cylinder. Releasing a catch allowed the barrel to be dropped down, taking the cylinder with it and so exposing the back ready for loading. At the same time as the barrel section was dropped, a simple linkage system pushed up the rod, which was fitted to the star-shaped end plate, so ejecting the cases. As the barrel was lowered a little further, the star piece was released and, under the pressure of a spring, snapped back into place, rendering the cylinder ready for reloading. This neat device was patented in the late 1860s by Smith & Wesson.

However, in 1873 the master patent expired and the field was open for all the gun makers. The Colt factory then produced its best known weapon. Listed officially as the Colt Single Action Army Revolver, it retained the traditional Colt silhouette and had a 7.5in barrel. It had a loading gate at the rear of the cylinder, and a spring-loaded ejector rod was housed beneath the barrel. This weapon acquired a range of titles, including the sixshooter, the Equalizer, and the Frontier.

In the 1878 model, Colt deserted its long established single-action

Above The Spanish manufacturer Astra produced this .357in caliber revolver, which is available with various barrel lengths. The cartridge is a more powerful version of the .38in. Special, which has a slightly longer case and a larger charge of powder.

system and produced a double-action revolver. Despite the United States Army not being impressed, the double-action system was here to stay, and many other revolver manufacturers adopted the system.

Faster loading rifles

The Civil War accelerated the introduction of breech loading into military circles with such weapons as the Sharps, Spencer, Burnside, Joslyn, and Starr carbines and rifles.

The Sharps used a vertically sliding breech block operated by a lever; the top edge was sharpened so as to slice the end off the paper cartridge as it closed, and it was fired by a hammer and percussion cap. The Starr used a linen cartridge and relied upon the force of the cap to pierce the linen and fire the powder. The Joslyn used a paper cartridge and closed the breech by a lifting flap carrying a gutta-percha seal. The Spencer and Burnside used metallic cartridges, the former a fairly ordinary rimfire,

Above **This design by Frederick Prince incorporated a system tried by several inventors. The lever beneath the barrel was turned and pushed to unlock the barrel from the fixed breech-piece and then slid forward to expose the chamber. After loading, the barrel was pulled back and turned so that the lugs on the breech-piece engaged in the chamber and locked the barrel in place.**

the latter a peculiar type which had to be loaded into the separate chamber base first, before the weapon could be closed.

The Winchester

The most famous of these lever-action designs was the Winchester. This began life as the Volcanic rifle, using an odd self-controlled round, which was simply a bullet with the base hollowed-out to carry a powder charge and a cap. Its drawback was that the bullet had insufficient room to carry a charge sufficient to generate a worthwhile velocity and

Above **Dating from 1860, the Spencer rifle used a tubular magazine inserted into the butt, feeding rimfire cartridges by a spring.**

the gun's poor performance led to the company's bankruptcy in 1857. It was bought by Oliver Winchester who knew little about guns but knew enough to hire a man who did — Benjamin T. Henry. Henry took the Volcanic and thoroughly redesigned it, adopting rimfire cartridges and later converting it to center-fire. In various forms the Winchester lever-action has remained in production ever since. The magazine is a tube running beneath the barrel. Pushing down the lever unlocks and opens the bolt, then operates a lifter to carry a cartridge up from the magazine to the chamber. Lifting the lever back into place causes the bolt to go forward and chamber the cartridge, and the lifter drops to line up with the magazine again. The movement of the bolt cocks an external hammer, which, when released, falls onto a firing pin in the bolt to fire the cartridge.

While these systems were adequate, none was sufficiently sound to attract interest from the major armies. The United States Army settled on the Springfield conversion and stayed with it until 1892. European armies, however, committed themselves to finding improved breech-loading systems, and examined the various options available. Three types became popular — the rolling block, the falling block, and the bolt.

Three breech-loading systems
The rolling block system was perfected by Remington in the United States in 1864. Designed for a

rimfire cartridge, it used a hinged block to close the breech; this block had a curved undersurface and behind it was the hammer. The hammer had a curved upper surface, so that as it fell, this surface passed beneath the block and securely supported it against the explosion of the cartridge.

The falling block was first developed by Henry Peabody of Boston in 1862. In this system the barrel was screwed into a rectangular box in which a solid breech block was pinned at its rear end. A lever beneath the weapon allowed this block to be swung down, exposing the mouth of the chamber, and a cartridge was inserted. Pulling up the lever raised the block to close the breech. The external hammer had to be cocked manually, and when released by the trigger, struck a curved firing pin in the block,

which in turn struck the rim of the cartridge and fired it.

In Switzerland Friedrich von Martini improved upon Peabody's idea by placing a firing pin and spring inside the breech block, and arranging for it to be cocked as the opening lever was operated. This did away with the need to cock the weapon as a separate action, and also allowed the use of the system with center-fire cartridges.

The bolt system was developed extensively by Mauser, who set about improving the Chassepot rifle in the hope of interesting the French. His principal improvement was in adapting the idea to a cased cartridge, and using a firing pin which was automatically cocked by the closing action of the bolt. The bolt had a prominent handle which was turned down in front of a lug on the receiver wall to lock the breech closed. It was also fitted at the rear with a safety catch which prevented the firing pin moving forward when applied.

Above **An American Winchester rifle, dating from 1873.**

Magazine rifle advances

Having settled upon a particular breech-loading system, the armies of the world turned to considering the adoption of a magazine rifle.

There were, of course, arguments against this; according to the opposition, given a full magazine, a soldier will simply fire off all the ammunition as soon as he sees an enemy a mile away. But the siege of Plevna (1877) showed that this was not necessarily so. At Plevna the Turkish defenders, each with 500 rounds, were armed with Winchester magazine carbines, and they repulsed several Russian attacks. This showed that any army without a magazine rifle was at a disadvantage.

The bolt-action rifle
James Paris Lee, a Scot who immigrated to the United States, had developed a bolt-action rifle. Beneath the bolt was a metal box, into which cartridges were placed on top of a spring. As the bolt was opened, the spring forced the cartridges up against a stop and the bolt pushed the top cartridge into the chamber as it closed. After firing, the opening of the bolt extracted the empty cartridge case, and the return stroke loaded a fresh round. The box could be detached for refilling, and the rifle was provided with a spare magazine for quick reloading in action. After severe testing, the Lee bolt and magazine were adopted by the British Army in the Lee-Metford rifle, Metford being the designer of the barrel.

Another innovation was the adoption of a jacketed bullet of

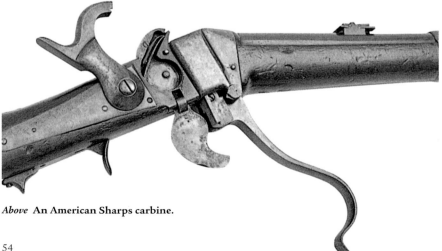

Above **An American Sharps carbine.**

Above The Krag Jorgensen rifle comes from Norway and dates from 1894.

.303in caliber. The small jacketed bullet was developed by Major Rubin of the Swiss Army. It had high velocity (giving better accuracy) and, due to its metal jacket, did not leave a coating of lead in the rifle barrel.

Meanwhile, the Germans applied to Mauser for something better. He adapted the box magazine idea and produced a rifle with a five-shot box magazine concealed inside the stock.

In Austria, Count Mannlicher designed another magazine rifle, slightly similar to the Mauser, but adopting a "straight-pull" bolt and a rotating magazine, still concealed inside the butt. The straight-pull bolt relied upon cam action: the bolt handle was pulled straight back, withdrawing a sleeve which drew a stud through a curved cam path in the bolt body, causing it to rotate. The Swiss adopted a straight-pull design, while the Japanese and Italians copied Mauser. Only the Scandinavians and the Americans

tried something different, in the Krag-Jorgensen rifle, which had an odd side-mounted magazine fed through a trapdoor.

The German Army returned to Mauser in 1898 and adopted his Gewehr 98, the ultimate Mauser with which they stayed until 1945. The only major step to be taken was the British adoption of the Lee-Enfield system. This used the same bolt action and magazine as before, but now allied to a new barrel developed by the Royal Small Arms Factory at Enfield. This was the result of the British adoption of cordite smokeless powder, which demanded a different system of rifling to get the best performance out of the weapon.

Bolt actions have changed very little during the twentieth century. The British L42A1 7.62mm sniping rifle in use today is the same Lee-Enfield action that was introduced in 1903 on the SMLE, with a few very small changes to simplify production.

Colt's rivals and successors

When Colt's master patent expired in 1857, there was a rush of competitors with designs roughly based on the Colt, although these were all percussion weapons.

Looking to the future, Horace Smith and Daniel Wesson patented a rimfire cartridge in 1854, and acquired another master patent covering any cylinder with chambers bored through from end to end. In 1857 they went into production with a .22in caliber rimfire-cartridge revolver, and subsequently enjoyed a virtual monopoly in the United States until 1869.

In 1868 the British Army changed to breech-loading weapons. As a result many of the Adams and Colt percussion weapons were adapted to

take a Boxer center-fire cartridge. As late as 1872 many units of the British Army were still being issued with single-shot percussion pistols, but after long discussions and some obstruction from the Duke of Cambridge, the Commander-in-Chief, revolvers were authorized for the Lancer units in 1877.

In August 1880 the pistol revolver B.L. Enfield (Mark 1), which fired a .45in cartridge, was officially approved for British Army use. These revolvers were not very popular, and a number of changes were made, including the addition of a safety catch, which is very unusual in revolver technology.

In 1886 the famous British name of Webley made its mark on the official revolver field when a revolver

produced by the company was adopted by the Royal Irish Constabulary. It was a rugged, sturdy weapon, firing a .442in cartridge, and it saw service with many police forces, including those in Australia and South Africa. In 1887 the Webley Pistol (Mark 1) was made the official revolver of the British Army. It was a .441in caliber and had a 4 inch (10 cm) barrel with a top beak.

Following this decision by the British Army, most European nations then examined their armament provision, and Belgium's arms center at Liège was kept extremely busy producing revolvers for Belgium's

Left **A close-up of the Gasser revolver, showing the simple, side-mounted ejector rod, which was used to push out the empty cases when the plate at the rear of the cylinder was pushed clear.**

Far Left **This is a Belgian-made 11mm version of the Gasser revolver. These weapons were designed by the Austrian Leopold Gasser in 1869, and they saw service with the armies of the Austro-Hungarian Empire. This example is in the Montenegrin style. Such models are comparatively common since the king of Montenegro ordered all his male subjects to purchase an example. Most are crudely decorated and have grips of horn or mother-of-pearl.**

own army and for many others as well. One easily recognizable product was the Gasser revolver, which was made for Montenegro, a small Balkan state. Most of these revolvers are massive and have what looks like a disproportionately small butt.

Another very recognizable revolver manufactured in Liège is the Galand, which was designed by a Frenchman and adopted by the Russian Navy. The distinguishing feature is the trigger guard, which extends forward under the barrel. Unlocked by a small catch, it swings forward and down, moving the entire barrel assembly forward. The cartridges pass through a plate at the rear of the cylinder, moves forward a short distance, and then stops while the cylinder continues to move forward. The distance of this movement is such that empty cases are pulled clear of the cylinder but the unfired cartridges, which are longer because the bullets are in situ, remain in place. Returning the trigger guard to the closed position then replaces the plate, and makes the cylinder ready for action.

The Russians also adopted a Smith & Wesson revolver, the Model 3 Russian First Model, which was slightly modified to take the Russian .44in cartridge. A Second Model which has as spur extending down from the trigger guard provides a firmer grip.

In 1895 the Russians changed to a smaller caliber weapon, the Nagant gas seal revolver. In this revolver the bullet is totally enclosed within the metal case, and the neck is slightly tapered. When it is loaded the tip of the cartridge projects slightly beyond the end of the cylinder. If the action is cocked the entire cylinder is pushed forward, which means that the tip of the cartridge engages with the barrel.

One of the largest and the ugliest military revolvers is the German Reichsrevolver, known for its big curving butt and large safety catch.

It was awkward to load, but this was probably because the German Army regarded hand guns as inferior weapons, to be used only in dire emergencies, or by charging cavalry.

Commercial Guns Shooting as a sport was gaining in popularity, and there was a continuing growth in small bore .22in revolvers. Numerous companies, particularly in the United States, supplied the target shooting market. The output of these companies was considerable, and Iver Johnson of New Jersey and Harrington & Richardson Inc. of Massachusetts made thousands of small bore revolvers, most of which

Above **The Webley .455/476in W.G. Army Revolver was produced in slightly different forms between 1886 and 1902. A solid weapon, intended primarily for military service, it was adapted for target shooting. The 6 inch (15 cm) barrel was well suited for accuracy.**

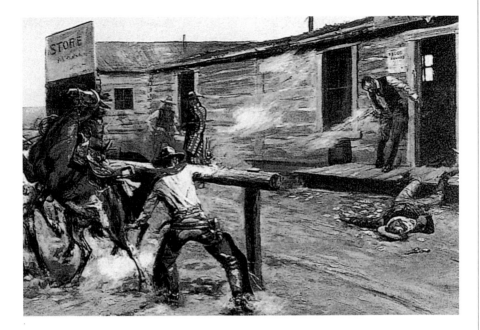

Above "The Gunfighters": a painting by Charles Russell (1902) depicting a difference of opinion being settled in the traditional Western manner of the 1880s by "Colonel Colt's Equalizer."

were top-break models with automatic ejection of the empty cases. Some manufacturers, including Smith & Wesson, Stevens, and Webley, produced single-shot target guns, many of which had longer barrels to improve accuracy.

Another fruitful market was for self-defense weapons. These were small revolvers with a caliber of .22in or .25in and small enough to drop into a pocket. There were two main types, which differed in the hammer fitting. The more common type had a spur on the hammer so that it could be cocked manually, although this could snag on clothing and possibly cock the action or even fire the revolver accidentally. The solution was the hammerless model. Yet another solution was to enclose the hammer within two shielding walls, with perhaps just the tip showing so that it was possible, but not easy, to cock the action manually.

Birth of the automatic

The development of effective automatic arms is attributed to an Austrian named Laumann, who had patented a mechanical bolt action pistol, and then converted it into a delayed blowback weapon. He had a small number of these pistols made by the Steyr-Mannlicher factory, and marketed them as the Schonberger pistol in 1892. It was in 8mm caliber.

Borchardt and Luger

Hugo Borchardt immigrated to America in the 1860s in the hopes of becoming a United States citizen. He worked for some time with Winchester designing revolvers, but none of his designs were produced, and Borchardt returned to Europe to work for the Hungarian arsenal.

There he saw a demonstration of Maxim's machine gun, and began thinking about an automatic pistol. He adopted Maxim's toggle lock, so that as the pistol barrel recoiled, the lock folded up to withdraw the bolt, at the same time winding up a clock-type spring. He also pioneered the use of a box magazine in the butt and developed the 7.63mm rimless necked cartridge, without which the design could not have worked. The result was the Borchardt pistol, made by Ludwig Loewe in Berlin. It was a cumbersome design, with a fragile and easily dislocated mechanism, but Borchardt seemed satisfied with it.

It was left to another Loewe employee, Georg Luger, to take the Borchardt and turn it into a more practical weapon. He cleaned up the

Above **The 8mm Roth-Steyr M1908 was the first automatic pistol to be adopted by the Austro-Hungarian Army.**

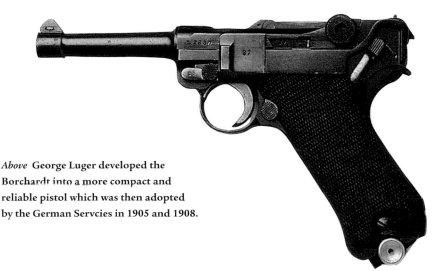

Above **George Luger developed the Borchardt into a more compact and reliable pistol which was then adopted by the German Servcies in 1905 and 1908.**

design, placing the return spring in the butt, and developed a somewhat powerful 7.65mm cartridge. He also changed the angle of the grip, so that the pistol pointed more instinctively and lay more comfortably in the hand. The result was the Luger pistol – properly called the Parabellum pistol – which appeared in 1900.

One reason for Luger to develop his pistol was the fact that the sales of the Borchardt had suffered from competition with Mauser, who produced his own superior automatic in 1896. The Mauser used the Borchardt cartridge, though it was renamed the 7.63mm Mauser cartridge. The pistol employed a recoiling bolt locked by lugs underneath it and unlocked by the short recoil of the barrel and frame.

The magazine was in front of the trigger, like the Mauser rifle, and was loaded through the open action by using a charger of ten cartridges.

Two other European designs of this period deserve mention. Theodor Bergmann employed a talented designer, Louis Schmeisser, to develop a simple blowback weapon and adapt the principle that the Skoda machine gun had pioneered. It was rather like the Mauser in layout, with a clip-fed magazine in front of the trigger, but the cartridge was a low-powered 6mm. The weapon was cheap, simple, and sold well. Schmeisser went on to develop locked-breech designs in the hopes of a military contract, and eventually succeeded in 1905, with a 9mm pistol which the Spanish Army adopted.

In 1907 the Austro-Hungarian Army approved the Roth-Steyr, and became the first major army to adopt an automatic pistol. This pistol adopted an entirely new method of locking the breech. The barrel was free to revolve inside an enveloping sleeve; behind it was the bolt, also enclosed in the sleeve, which formed the body of the pistol. At the front of the barrel were two helical lugs, which engaged in grooves in the inner surface of the sleeve. When the barrel recoiled, and locked to the bolt, it pulled these lugs along the slots, which turned the barrel through about 30 degrees; this caused the barrel to unlock itself from the bolt, whereupon it stopped moving, allowing the bolt to continue rearward, extract the empty case and then, driven by a spring, move forward to load the next round. An odd feature was that the magazine was loaded through the top of the weapon by opening the bolt and then using a charger of ten rounds and driving them down into the magazine. It was also odd in that the firing pin was only partially cocked as the weapon reloaded. Full cocking involved pulling the trigger, which first completed the cocking of the firing pin, and then released it. It is said that this was insisted upon by the military because the pistol was for issue to cavalry and they were afraid of what might happen if a trooper had his finger on the trigger of a cocked pistol if his horse suddenly became skittish.

The "Original Browning"

In the United States, John Browning developed a simple blowback pistol in .32in caliber, a cartridge he had developed especially for it. He was unable to find an American manufacturer, and took the design to Europe where he arranged with the Fabrique Nationale d'Armes de Guerre of Liège, Belgium, to manufacture his designs. His first model became known as the Original Browning, or the Model 1900, and he soon followed it with an even simpler model.

This became the Model 1903, one of the simplest and most successful pistol designs ever made. However, the cartridge was not sufficiently powerful for military use, so Browning went back to his design office to develop a locked breech pistol capable of firing a heavy load. This time, there was a more receptive atmosphere at home in the United States, and the Colt company took up his military design. The basic construction was similar to that of the 1903 pistol — frame and slide — but the hammer was on the outside

Above The influence of John Moses Browning on self-loading pistol design spanned a quarter of a century until his death in 1926. His last design was refined to become the Browning GP35 (direct).

of the frame, where a glance could reveal whether or not the pistol was cocked. The barrel was held to the frame by a loose link, so that it could

move rearward and, due to the link, downward. On top were two lugs, which mated with two slots in the inner surface of the slide. With the pistol loaded, the lugs and slots engaged; on firing, the recoil force drove barrel and slide back, and then locked together for a short distance. Then, due to the link, the rear of the barrel moved downwards, so withdrawing the lugs from the slide.

Automatic rifles

By the early years of this century the automatic machine gun had come into use, and inventors subsequently began contemplating how to make a rifle automatic in its action so that a soldier could simply maintain his aim, and keep pulling the trigger.

Indeed, the Danish Navy had adopted an automatic rifle as early as the 1890s, though this trend failed to last and automatic rifles later became replced with light machine guns. Other designs were put forward, notably the Italian Cei-Rigotti of 1900 and the Mexican Mondragon of 1907, but they proved cumbersome and too complicated to withstand active service. It was not until 1932, when the United States Army settled on the Garand, that a major army adopted an automatic rifle as standard.

This invention of John Garand, who was then working at the Springfield Armory, was a .30in gas operated rifle that tapped a small portion of the propellant gas from the barrel and used it to drive back a piston. This was linked to the bolt, so as to rotate and open it, and then thrust it back against a spring. After the thrust died away, the spring forced the bolt and piston back, collecting a cartridge from the magazine and loading it, simultaneously cocking the firing mechanism. The magazine held eight rounds in a clip; after the last round had been fired, the bolt stayed open and the clip was ejected ready for reloading. Though somewhat heavier than the Springfield it replaced, the Garand was a robust and reliable weapon, which served the United States Army well for over 30 years.

The Garand was strictly an 11 semiautomatic, rather than a true automatic weapon — it fired one shot and reloaded, waiting for the firer to pull the trigger for the next shot. Automatic fire could have been provided, but was not practical; firing such a powerful cartridge at high

rates caused a hand-held weapon to become uncontrollable and simply waste ammunition.

The Soviets had discovered this already. In the 1920s they had

Above **A United States infantryman on exercise, armed with his Colt M16A2 rifle, a handy combat weapon.**

Above **The Simonov SKS 46.**

adopted small numbers of the Federov automatic rifle, designed in 1916 around the Japanese 6.5mm rifle cartridge, large numbers of which had been captured by Russia during the Russo-Japanese War of 1904–1905. This low-powered round produced a weapon that was more controllable, but it proved somewhat fragile and, in the chaos of the revolution and its aftermath, the idea was abandoned. When the Americans put Garand into service, however, Soviet interest was rekindled and two designs, the Simonov of 1936 and the Tokarev of 1938, were produced. Both fired the full-power 7.62mm rifle cartridge, and both proved to be too much of a handful and too fragile for general service. The Tokarev was finally only used as a specialist sniping rifle.

The German Army also looked closely at the automatic rifle concept.

Mauser had made experimental weapons during World War I, but none were acceptable. Though various inventors put up ideas in between the wars, it was not until 1940 that the Army finally put forward an official demand for such a weapon. The answer was the Walther G41, an odd weapon that used the muzzle blast to drive a cup

Below **American troops using the AR15 in 1968.**

Above **The Colt M16A2 rifle (model 701), standard United States Army issue.**

forward to actuate the reloading mechanism. It was not a success, being temperamental and badly balanced, and production was soon stopped despite the rifle being used until 1945.

A more significant development was the FG42, a special rifle developed for the German parachute forces. Like the G41, this used the standard 7.92mm rifle cartridge, a powerful round, but clever design made it almost controllable in automatic fire. As a single shot weapon, the bolt was closed and locked before firing; in the automatic mode, the bolt stayed open between bursts, allowing the barrel to cool. It was laid out in a straight line instead of having the traditionally dropped butt, so that the recoil went into the shoulder directly, and had little tendency to lift the muzzle away from the target. The magazine fed from the side, metal and plastic were used in its manufacture, and the whole thing weighed less than ten pounds.

Unfortunately, it was expensive and slow to manufacture; it was also a Luftwaffe rather than an Army weapon (the parachute troops came under the German Air Force), so it never went into army service and so no more than 7,000 were ever made.

Postwar rifles

Except for a few short-lived experiments, the remaining armies of World War II went to war with slightly improved versions of the bolt-action rifles they had carried in 1914–1918. It was not until the war was over that serious work began on replacing all these rifles with automatic weapons.

The first automatic weapon to go into service was the Soviet Kalashnikov AK47, designed around a new 7.62mm short cartridge that probably owed something to the German assault rifle round. The Kalashnikov was simple and tough, could fire single shots or automatically at 600 rounds a minute, was gas operated, and used a 30-shot magazine. It is probably the most prolifically produced and distributed rifle in history, upwards of 40 million having been turned out in the past 40 years alone. Production of the Kalashnikov and of its copies still continues in many countries.

Britain was also impressed by the German short-case cartridge, and developed a 7mm round and a rifle to accompany it in the last 1940s. Thus the EM2 (Enfield Model 2) was

Above and Below **The Walther WA 2000, complete with special Zeiss sight.**

Below **The 7.62mm Galil semi-automatic, produced by Israel Military Industries.**

produced, a revolutionary design years ahead of its time. The layout of the rifle was what is known (for no very good reason) as a "bullpup," meaning that the actual breech is located right at the butt end of the rifle, under the firer's ear. In a bullpup, with the breech against the end of the butt, the length of the breech and barrel is the length of the rifle. The same length of barrel can therefore be accommodated inside a shorter overall length.

The EM2 was approved for service as the Rifle No. 9 in 1951, but it was canceled before production. At that time, the first stirrings of NATO standardization were in the air, and a common small arms round was among the first priorities. The Canadian and French armies were favorably disposed to the British 7mm round, but the Americans were implacably against it. Eventually, for the sake of NATO amity, Britain gave up its rifle and cartridge, adopting the American 7.62mm cartridge and the Belgian Fabrique National FAL rifle to go with it. The United States set about reworking the Garand to make it capable of automatic fire, and gave it a 20-round box magazine, calling the result the 7.62mm M14 rifle.

The remainder of NATO settled for gas operated conventional

automatic rifles firing the standard 7.62mm cartridge, and matters might have rested there were it not for the outbreak of conflict in Vietnam. In the intervening years prior to war, a private company in the United States, Armalite, had developed a lightweight gas operated rifle firing a new .233in cartridge. This was largely due to the United States Army searching for a new rifle that would give a higher first round hit probability. Various solutions were tested, but the general consensus favored a light rifle firing a lighter bullet, so that aim disturbance due to recoil was minimal.

This led Armalite to develop its .233in rifle, which was called the AR15. During the Vietnam War, the United States Air Force purchased a number of these for use by airfield guards in Vietnam; they were seen by troops of the United States Army, who opinioned that these rifles were just what was needed for jungle warfare. More were purchased, and, to cut a long story short, by the late 1960s the United States Army had decided that the AR15, now known as the M16, would be their standard infantry rifle. This made nonsense of NATO standardization and also of their earlier refusal of the 7mm cartridge.

Faced with this, the rest of NATO had to think about its infantry armament. Most of the rifles adopted in the early 1950s were approaching the end of their economic lives, and by the 1980s would need replacement, so rifle designers began looking at the .223in (or, as it was now known, 5.56mm) cartridge. Although smaller than the standard 7.62mm caliber used hitherto, it had a high velocity and was amply lethal. The only drawback was that it had

Above **The SIG 550 Sniper rifle.**

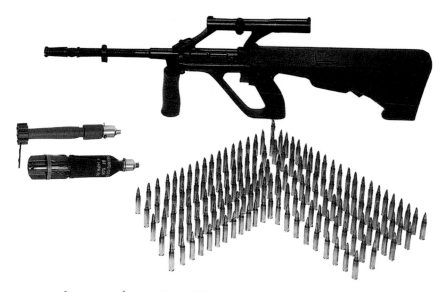

Above **The Steyr-Mannlicher AUG is an extremely advanced 5.6mm design with interchangeable barrels, so the rifle can be swiftly converted.**

poor performance above 440 to 550 yards (400 to 500 meters) range. A number of designs appeared from private manufacturers, such as Beretta, Fabrique Nationale, and Heckler & Koch, but, rather than jump at any of them, NATO decided on a long and exhaustive test in the late 1970s, aimed at settling the question of what cartridge they would adopt as standard.

After four years of testing, the result was the standardization of the 5.56mm cartridge, but with a heavier bullet. With this settled, armies could adopt new designs, and the British were among the first with their SA80. However, perhaps the most astonishing of the European 5.56mm rifles was the Austrian AUG (Army

Universal Gun) developed by Steyr-Mannlicher. This, too, was a bullpup design, introduced in the early 1980s, but was built in modular form so that several of its parts could be changed. The whole weapon is based on strong plastic housing; the barrel can be quickly removed and exchanged for one of four different lengths, giving the options of submachine gun, carbine, rifle, or light machine gun. The receiver, inside which the bolt works, incorporates a carrying handle with built-in optical sight.

Care and Acquisition

Care and Acquisition

Most countries allow a collector to keep as many antique firearms as desired, although a few insist that they be registered. The difficulty lies in defining the word "antique" — and for every definition, it is possible to find exceptions!

Attempts have been made to define antique firearms by their type of action, by the type of ammunition that they use, and by the date of manufacture. In Britain it is possible to own a Colt Navy percussion revolver made in 1852, but not a copy made in Italy in 1982 even though apart from the materials and some modifications for the purpose of manufacture, they are identical revolvers. It is assumed by law makers that if somebody purchases a modern copy, it is because they plan to fire it.

In some European countries, the Snider rifle is regarded as an antique, but in others it is not. Some countries do not allow private individuals to own handguns that use military caliber ammunition, so that in some countries, for example, one may not own a pistol that fires 9mm Parabellum ammunition. However, if the cartridge case and breech are slightly modified, the ammunition is no longer the same as the military cartridge, and it is legal to own the gun.

In the United States laws vary from state to state, although there are some federal laws that apply to all states. With so many possible legal combinations and opinions, the best advice to be given is to make sure that you inform yourself of the law for your area, state, or country before even attempting to acquire your first handgun. The local police should be in a position to advise, but as firearm legislation is a complex subject, it may be necessary to go to a fairly senior level to get reliable answers. Even then, the advice may be wrong. If possible, get a written statement setting out the position. You should also contact any local or national societies involved with collecting or shooting because such societies are often better informed on the law than the police.

Care of acquisitions

Some preparation is necessary before you make your first acquisition. You must consider factors such as security, recording, and insurance of your acquisitions.

Right These may look like a Luger 08 pistol and a P38, but they are, in fact, totally harmless copies. A large range of such copies is available, many of which are made to fire blanks, and most are so realistic that they can be identified as replicas only when they are handled. Some are "soft air" weapons, which fire a harmless plastic pellet.

Above A British Army issue .38in revolver, which saw service in World War II. It looks a little worn and battered. Close inspection, however, will reveal that the firing pin is missing from the hammer, and that the barrel is blocked and the cylinder has been made unusable. It is an officially deactivated weapon, freely available in Britain.

Security

The intrinsic value of guns and the importance of preventing criminal use are both factors that make it essential that guns are safe and secure. Safes are an obvious storage point, but, of course, this means that the collection will not be seen on open display. Many types of special cabinets with security glass doors and panels as well as alarms are available. Trigger locks can ensure that actions are not worked, and, of course, ammunition and guns should never be kept together unless under strict supervision.

Display

Display and security are closely connected, and compromise is the key to their relationship. If weapons are kept under glass it is important to ensure that they are not in direct sunlight, for the sun is a bleaching agent that lightens and dries wood. Ideally, weapons should not be handled with bare hands, for human sweat is a powerful rusting agent. Even contemporary bluing is affected by some sweat, and thin cotton gloves should be worn at all times when handling weapons. The material on which guns lie should be chemically inactive.

Right **The new style of self-loading pistol, the Heckler & Koch VP 70 9mm has, like the Mauser and Lugar, got a plastic stock, which can be attached to give greater stability when aiming. This German-made weapon has a large magazine capacity of 18 rounds, and it can be set to fire shots in bursts of three. For this reason its ownership is prohibited in some countries.**

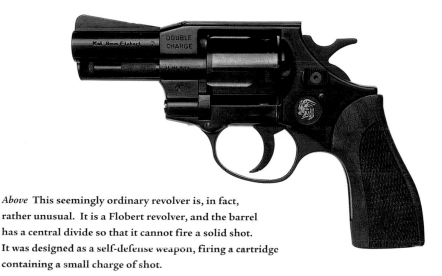

Above This seemingly ordinary revolver is, in fact, rather unusual. It is a Flobert revolver, and the barrel has a central divide so that it cannot fire a solid shot. It was designed as a self-defense weapon, firing a cartridge containing a small charge of shot.

Recording

It is well worth creating a fairly full catalog right from the start of your collection. Quite apart from keeping a personal record, if an item is unfortunately stolen, you will be able to provide your insurance company and the police with a full description. The important details to note are the small features that can distinguish two similar items. Numbers, marks, scratches, wear, measurements, weight, and replacement parts can all help to identify a particular weapon. Catalog descriptions will be greatly enhanced by the addition of a photograph. One full-length shot together with one or two close-ups of any particular features will usually suffice. Details of the price and place of purchase and subsequent disposal should all be recorded.

Insurance

Insurance companies will require a complete list of the items, with full descriptions and a valuation. It may be necessary to obtain an authenticated valuation from a professional. In general, it is customary to fix the insurance about a third higher than actual value, for it is inevitable that the cost of replacing an item will exceed the original price paid.

Checking acquisitions

Dismantling a modern handgun is, with one or two exceptions, fairly easy and straightforward, but there

Above A way of stabilizing the barrel during rapid firing is to put a muzzle brake on the barrel that has a slit that allows some of the gas to escape in a direction that counteracts the recoil. The Mark 1 Ruger .22in LR pistol shown here has just such a device fitted.

Above Weights that help to hold the barrel steady are often used, as on this sporting pistol, a Walther .22in Olympia. The weights are of most value in rapid fire events, when the recoil tends to raise the barrel — the weights counteract this effect.

are a few basic rules that must be followed. The first, to which there can never be any exception, is the proving of the weapon, which simply means making sure that the weapon is unloaded. In the case of a revolver, check the cylinder to see that it is empty. With self-loading pistols the magazine should be removed from the weapon, and the slide pulled back to expose the breech to ensure that there are no rounds in place. While this is being done the weapon should always be pointed in a safe direction so that should there be an accidental discharge, there is no chance of anybody being hit.

It is good policy to put the parts on a lid or tray to minimize the chances of their falling onto the floor. If they are placed in sequence as they are removed, replacement is much easier.

The tools required are fairly minimal, but the golden rule is that screwdrivers and turnscrews of the appropriate size must always be used — too large or too small a blade can slip to produce a nasty scratch. Cleaning and oiling will probably be all that is required, and the use of silicone cloths to wipe over the weapon after reassembly, is not a bad idea.

Acquiring handguns

There are three main sources of supply — dealers, auction houses, and fellow collectors.

Dealers

Good dealers will give good service and take only a reasonable profit. They will also guarantee that the object sold is exactly as described, and if no such guarantee is forthcoming, look for dealers who will supply one. Dealers have time to attend shows, visit auctions, and follow up interesting leads, which all take up time the average collector does not usually have. Dealers can therefore have an important place in the collector's life.

Auction houses

You should bear in mind that most of a dealer's stock will be purchased at auction, and if you, too, buy at auction, you will save money by cutting out the dealer's profit. Auction houses depend on their reputation and expertise to attract business, so the fact that an object is offered for auction suggests that it is probably correct. Though mistakes do occur, auction houses usually have clauses in their terms and conditions that will allow the purchaser to claim back the cost if an object is found not to be as cataloged. Bidding for items without viewing is not to be recommended and if an agent or dealer cannot view the sale on your

Right **Most firearms produced by the Stevens Arms Company were top-break models, with the barrel folding down as shown here. Many of the company's early firearms are .22in caliber.**

behalf, you should ask for a condition report from the auctioneer. This report should give a full description of the object with all faults, doubts, as well as some advice on the likely price. If you decide that an item in an auction is of interest, it is important to pre-determine your top bid.

Below **An engraving from British publication *The Graphic*, dating from 1881. It is intresting to see the traditional shooting position of the period. The bent arm was adequate for revolvers but not self-loading pistols.**

Collectors

There are many societies and clubs devoted to the collecting, study, and use of handguns, and contact with these groups is always worthwhile. The exchange of information, the chance to see collections, and the buying and selling that takes place among the members all make the cost of the subscription a good investment. Many antique fairs offer space to such societies, which is another reason for attending such events. Trips to various museums and exhibitions are never wasted

Right The grips have been removed from this
Colt Python .357in Magnum revolver to show the source
of the power — the main spring, which forces the hammer
down to strike the primer. The rib along the top of the
barrel helps to disperse the heat created by the shots,
because the barrel can get very hot indeed.

either, since every visit can add
something to the knowledge and
understanding of the subject.

Care of the collection is obviously
important, for damage and wear will
reduce the value in varying degrees.
Restoration and repairs usually have
the same effect, as most collectors
prefer the items to be in as original
condition as possible. Snapping the
action of revolvers is dangerous
because it can damage the hammer,
nipples, and springs. Furthermore
actions should not be left cocked,
for the continual tension on the
springs may cause fractures. It is
also not good policy to leave pistols
in holsters, especially leather ones,
as reactions between the leather and
metal can damage the surface of the
metal. Treated with care and respect,
a collection will give hours of
pleasure, and may also represent a
surprisingly valuable investment in
times to come.

A–Z of Rifles and Small Arms

A–Z of Rifles and Small Arms

A large part of firearms development has its roots in military requirements. However, the advent of the nuclear age has witnessed sports and firearms enthusiasts entering the fray.

Abadie

Abadie was a Belgian gunsmith whose name is associated with a hinged loading gate and safety device used on various European revolvers from about 1880 to 1900. In this device the loading gate is linked with the pistol hammer so that opening the gate to load or unload the pistol draws the hammer back to a half-cock position, and locks it there so as to prevent it accidentally falling forward and possibly firing a cartridge during the loading process.

Adler

This was a German automatic pistol patented by Hermsdorff in 1905. It was a blowback pistol firing a unique 7mm bottle-necked cartridge and using a reciprocating bolt in the receiver.

The patented feature was the method of construction of the receiver, whereby the top and sides could be swung up and back to expose the breech and bolt for cleaning.

AK47

This Soviet automatic rifle was developed by Mikhail Kalashnikov shortly after World War II. It was designed around a 7.62mm short cartridge developed at the end of the war, and based on the similar German 7.92mm short assault rifle round.

Using a short cartridge allows the rifle to be smaller and more compact due to the lower recoil energy and the shorter reloading stroke required. The AK47 uses gas operation, a piston above the barrel being driven back by a small amount of gas tapped from the barrel. This piston strikes a bolt carrier which starts to the rear, a cam surface inside it rotating the bolt so as to unlock it from the breech. Carrier and bolt then go to the rear,

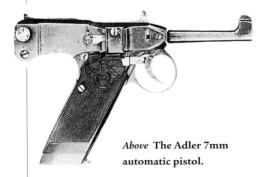

Above **The Adler 7mm automatic pistol.**

extracting the empty cartridge case and ejecting it. A return spring then forces carrier and bolt forward, chambering a fresh cartridge from the 30-shot magazine. As the carrier is forced home, it revolves the bolt and locks it. Pressure on the trigger now releases a hammer to strike the firing pin in the bolt, firing the weapon. A selector lever permits firing single shots or full-automatic fire at a rate of about 600 rounds per minute.

Above **The Soviet-designed AK47 Kalashnikov, the most prolifically manufactured rifle in armament history. This example came from China.**

Albini-Braendlin

A .60in caliber rimfire rifle was developed by Augusto Albini, an Admiral in the Italian Navy. Albini designed the rifle in 1865, using a hinged breech section which could be lifted up to permit loading of the cartridge, after which it was dropped back into the action so as to align with the bore. An external hammer then struck a firing pin to fire the cartridge. The system could either be applied to a new weapon, or could be applied to existing muzzle-loading rifles to convert them into breech loading rifles.

Albini had the rifle manufactured by the Braendlin Armoury Company of Birmingham, England. It was adopted by the Italian Navy in 1866, followed by the Belgian Army, and the armies of Bavaria and Würtemberg. In addition, the Belgian Army converted numbers of muzzle-loaders to the Albini system.

Above A Japanese 38th Year Carbine, designed by Arisaka.

Apache

This was a type of pocket revolver invented by the Liège gunsmith Louis Dolne in the 1870s. It was a pepperbox revolver, the cylinder being much longer than the 7mm pinfire cartridge so that each chamber served as its own barrel. The butt was a steel or brass casting which was pierced with finger-holes and could be folded beneath the cylinder and frame. In this position the owner could grasp the cylinder in the palm of his hand and slip his fingers through the holes in the butt, the result being a very serviceable knuckle-duster. In addition, a dagger blade was hinged to the frame in front of the cylinder and could be folded into the frame or extended in front of the pistol, whereupon the weapon could function as a dagger.

Arisaka

This was a Japanese service rifle, used from 1897 to 1945, and designed by Colonel Arisaka. The Arisaka rifle is largely a Mauser copy, though there

are some differences in the design of the bolt. Numerous variants were produced over the years, which were first identified by the symbol and year of the current monarch's reign. The nomenclature was later changed to conform to the Japanese calender.
Meiji 30th Year (1897): 6.5mm infantry rifle.
Meiji 30th Year Carbine (1897): As above, but shorter.
Meiji 38th Year (1905): 6.5mm rifle designed after the Russo-Japanese War. Despite improved safety catch and bolt design, this was still considered a long rifle.
Meiji 38th Year Carbine: Similar changes were made in the cavalry weapon in 1905.
Meiji 44th Year Carbine (1911): Similar to the 38th Year but with a folding bayonet beneath the fore-end.

Armalite

The company's first success came with the design of the AR-5 Survival Rifle for the United States Air Force. This was a simple lightweight bolt

action rifle chambered for the .22in Hornet cartridge, which could be rapidly dismantled into its component parts and packed into the hollow butt. When so packed, the rifle could actually float if dropped in water. The AR-7 was a civil version of the AR-5. It was a blowback autoloader chambered for the .22in Long Rifle round.

In 1955 Armalite began development of an assault rifle chambered for the 7.62mm NATO cartridge. This rifle used an unusual gas system in that the gas tapped from the barrel was piped back and vented directly into the bolt carrier. This drove the carrier back and, by cam action, rotated and unlocked the bolt. The whole weapon was laid out in a straightline configuration, which generates less of an upward couple when fired, allowing the weapon to be kept more accurately on target when on automatic fire.

In 1958 the AR-15 rifle was produced. Designed by Stoner, this was chambered for the 5.56mm cartridge. In military service the AR-15 was designated the M16.

In the AR-18 rifle, the system of gas operation changed. A conventional piston and rod

Above **United States infantryman carrying an Armalite AR-15 in Vietnam (belts are of a different gun).**

mounted above the barrel were used, whereby the piston rod was thrust back against the bolt carrier. The gun body is of pressed steel, suitably welded, while many of the major components are steel stampings rather than expensive forgings. The design could be manufactured by light engineering shops with no gun-making knowledge or facilities.

Astra

The Astra name was first used in 1911 for a 7.65mm copy of the Browning 1903 automatic pistol, but it became prominent in 1921 when the Spanish Army adopted the Astra Model 400 as their service Model 1921 pistol.

This model was derived from the Campo-Giro design, and was a blowback automatic chambered for the 9mm Bergmann-Bayard cartridge, known in Spain as the 9mm Largo. The pistol's shape was unique, a long tubular barrel and jacket resembling a water pistol more than a firearm. This outline was perpetuated in subsequent models — notably the Model 600 in 9mm Parabellum.

The name was also used for a series of pistols based on the Mauser C/96 Military pattern which was introduced in 1928. Externally resembling the Mauser, the internal mechanism was simplified and three variants were produced: the first used a 20-shot integral magazine, the second a 10- or 20-shot removable magazine, and the third chambered for the 9mm Largo.

In the 1950s the company began production of revolvers under the name Astra Cadix. These are solid frame models with swing-out cylinders, based generally on Smith & Wesson practice.

Above **The Spanish company Astra produced a considerable range of pistols, all of which are of good quality. They were manufactured in a range of calibers — the version of the Model 4000 shown here is 7.65mm.**

Auto-Mag

This was an American automatic pistol manufactured by the TDE Corporation of El Monte, California. This pistol was designed around a "wildcat" cartridge, the .44in Auto Magnum, which was produced by marrying a .44in revolver bullet to a cut-down 7.62mm NATO rifle cartridge case. In the early 1960s Max Gera began work on an automatic pistol designed to fire this cartridge. This pistol was eventually announced as the Auto-Mag early in 1970.

The Auto-Mag is a recoil-operated pistol with a rotating bolt head controlled by cam tracks in the pistol frame. Firing a .44in 240 grain bullet, it develops a muzzle velocity of 1640 ft/sec and a muzzle energy of 1455 lbs.

The Auto-Mag Company of Pasadena was set up to make the gun in late 1970, though at that time

Above **Harry Sanford's Auto-Mag was hampered by a lack of factory ammunition. The first cartridges were made from cut down .308in Winchester rifle brass.**

commercial ammunition was not available, and purchasers of the gun had to make their own rounds.

Since the time the company got into financial difficulties, the patents and rights for the pistol have passed through several hands. The latest information is that the TDE Corporation is making the pistol, while the High-Standard Company is assuming responsibility for distribution. The pistol is available in .44in Auto Magnum caliber and also in .357in Auto Magnum, a similar combination of .357in revolver bullet and cut-down 7.62mm case. It is a powerful pistol and has gained popularity as a hunting weapon.

Above **The Bär repeating pistol; the chamber block held four cartridges.**

Bang

The Danish designer of an automatic rifle, Bang took out a series of patents from 1901 up to the early 1920s which covered a rifle operated by muzzle blast. A sliding cone over the rifle muzzle was driven forward by the rush of gas following the bullet ejection, and this movement was communicated via an operating rod to a breech bolt carrier unit. By a lever arrangement the carrier was driven to the rear, and cam surfaces within the carrier rotated the breech bolt, unlocking it from the barrel, and then opening the breech. A return spring then forced the carrier back to load a fresh cartridge from the box magazine, and then rotate and lock the bolt. The muzzle cone was repositioned at the same time, ready for the next shot.

The Bang rifle later reappeared in a lighter and improved form. Lightening the weapon, however,

impaired the robustness. Bang made no further attempts to improve the weapon thereafter.

Bär

The Bär pistol was a self-cocking weapon with two barrels measuring two inches. Behind the barrels, in the solid frame, was a rectangular block bored with four superposed chambers, the top pair of which was aligned with the pistol's two barrels. This block was centrally pivoted on its longitudinal axis and could be swung 90 degrees sideways so as to expose the chambers for loading.

The block was then swung back and aligned with the frame, after which the first pull on the trigger would cock the internal hammer and fire the top cartridge through the top barrel. The second pull automatically realigned the internal firing pin to fire the cartridge in the second (lower) chamber, discharging the bullet through the lower barrel. The block was then rotated 180 degrees to bring the two bottom chambers to the top and into alignment with the barrels. These were then fired in the same manner.

Bayonne

The original Bayonne designs were based on the well-known Browning blowback patterns, and were in

6.35mm, 7.65mm, and 9mm Short calibers.

The Model A was a 6.35mm copy of the Browning 1906, with triple safety.

Model B, also in 6.35mm, differed in appearance, having an open-topped slide which exposed the upper surface of the barrel.

Model C in 7.65mm and 9mm Short resembled the Browning Model 1910, because the recoil spring round the barrel was retained by a muzzle locking ring.

Model D was a C with lengthened slide and barrel.

New models introduced since 1945 are the 6.35mm Model E, resembling the Model D; the Model R, again resembling the Model D but having an external hammer and chambered for 7.65mm ACP or 7.65mm French Longue cartridges; the Model D Para, chambered for the 9mm Parabellum cartridge and internally modified so as to incorporate breech locking controlled by a rotating barrel; and the Model F, a .22 pistol generally using the Model D frame but with a variety of barrel lengths for target shooting.

This company also produced the Echasa Model GZ for the Spanish company of Echave & Arizmendi; this was a slightly modified Model D.

The Model F, when provided with an external hammer, is sold as the Le Chasseur.

The Model C became Le Cavalier, the Model D Le Gendarme, and the Model R Le Militaire.

All these pistols were commercial, but in the 1970s the Model R Para was slightly modified in order to accept a special 15-shot magazine and was issued to the French Army as the Model PA-15.

Right **A French pistol, made by Manufacture d'Armes Automatique de Bayonne and known, in consequence, as the MAB. The model illustrated is a Model D, which was available in .32in or .380in caliber.**

Beholla

This 7.65mm automatic pistol was developed by Becker & Hollander of Suhl, Germany, in 1915. It was taken into use by the German Army as a substitute standard weapon, the entire production of which went to the Army, and none ever being offered commercially. By army orders, the design was later contracted to other manufacturers, and made as the Leonhardt, Menta, and Stenda. The latter version, by Stendawerke, was continued into the post-1918 period as a commercial design.

The Beholla was a fixed-barrel blowback pistol of no particular merit, but it was unusual in its method of assembly. The barrel was retained in the pistol frame by a cross-pin which had to be driven out through holes specially made in the slide. As a result, it was not possible to dismantle the pistol without using a bench vice and thin punch to drive out the pin, a defect which meant that field cleaning must have been cursory. Apart from this, the Beholla was a robust and serviceable weapon. Study of serial numbers suggests that upwards of 100,000 copies of this weapon may have been made under various names.

Beretta

The first Beretta pistol was the Model 1915. It was a 7.65mm blowback, which exhibited the standard Beretta

Above **This Beretta Model 1951 E is one of a contract that supplied Egypt. This firm now supplies the United States with their standard 9mm sidearm.**

Left Made in both 9mm
and 7.65mm calibers,
the Beretta Model 1915
has a manual safety catch
mounted on the left-hand
side. On the 9mm version
of this model, the safety
catch acted directly on the
internal hammer.

Left Made in both 9mm
and 7.65mm calibers,
the Beretta Model 1915
has a manual safety catch
mounted on the left-hand
side. On the 9mm version
of this model, the safety
catch acted directly on the
internal hammer.

Right One of the
smallest Beretta pistols
ever made was the Model
950 .22in Sport pistol,
which was also available
in 6.35mm caliber.

characteristic — the front of the
slide was cut away so as to expose
the upper surface of the fixed
pistol barrel.

The 9mm version of Model 1915,
chambered for the Glisenti cartridge,
had a stronger recoil spring plus a
buffer spring to soften the slide
return action. This model is easily
recognized by the large safety catch
and the presence of an ejection port
in the top of the slide.

The Model 1915/19 was an
improved Model 1915 in which
the front ends of the slide sides
were swept over the barrel to carry
the foresight. This model was
produced only in 7.65mm caliber.

The Model 1919 was the first
pistol to be offered commercially; it
was simply a 6.35mm version of the
1915/19 with the addition of a grip
safety in the butt backstrap.

The Model 1923 was a 1915/19
modified in order to use an external
hammer. Chambered for the 9mm
Glisenti round, it was only made in
small numbers. It was followed by the

Model 1931, which reverted to the 1915 pattern, but added an external hammer. Most of these were issued to the Italian Navy, and are generally found with wooden grips with a small medallion carrying the naval emblem, RM divided by an anchor. Those sold commercially have black plastic grips with the monogram PB.

The Model 1934 is probably the most common Beretta, having been made in vast numbers for the Italian Army. It is little more than a 1931 chambered for the 9mm Short cartridge. Military weapons will be found marked RE (Army), RA (Air Force), or RM (Navy) while police weapons are marked PS.

The Model 1935 was a 1934 in 7.65mm caliber, used by the Air Force and Navy. It was sold commercially as the Model 935.

Since 1945, several commercial models have been sold under various names — Jaguar, Minx, Puma, etc. These are almost all variants of the

Above **Beretta's SS06 rifles can cope with the higher-powered .375in Holland & Holland and .458in Winchester Magnum cartridges.**

basic 1934 design, chambered for .22in, 6.35mm, or 7.65mm cartridges.

The last important military design was the Model 951, or Brigadier, which was the first locked-breech pistol from Beretta. The general form is still that of the M1 934, but it is larger in all dimensions, and chambered for the 9mm Parabellum cartridge. Breech locking is done by a wedge beneath the barrel which holds barrel and slide together until it is unlocked by striking the frame after a short recoil — very similar to the system used on the Walther P-38 pistol.

In 1977 several new designs were announced, including the Model 81 in 7.65mm, the Model 84 in 9mm Short, and the Model 92 in 9mm

Parabellum; these are all fitted with double-action lockwork, and have large capacity magazines, the model 92 taking 15 shots and the other 12 shots.

The Beretta BM59 uses the basic Garand mechanism but with a new 7.62mm barrel, a 20-shot removable magazine which can be topped up from chargers while in place on the rifle, a new trigger and firing mechanism, and a grenade launcher on the muzzle. Three variant models were produced: the standard; the Alpini with a cut-down stock, pistol grip, and folding butt; and the

Below **The top of Beretta's range is their side-by-side Molde 445 EEL, featuring ornate silverwork and beautiful engraving of the big game hunter's quarry — lions, leopards, water buffalo, and elephant.**

Parachutist's model, which is much like the Alpini, but with a removable grenade launcher and flash-hider.

When the 5.56mm cartridge became popular, Beretta built a completely new rifle. The AR70 is an assault rifle, gas-operated via an overhead piston and bolt carrier, and is very much in the modem idiom, being largely made of steel pressings welded together. It can fire single shots or automatic fire at a rate of 700 rpm.

At present, the Beretta company offers a single-barrel trap gun; double-barreled guns in side-by-side and over-and-under configuration in 12 and 20 gauge, with barrels ranging from 26 inches to 30 inches; and a gas-operated automatic shotgun in 12 and 20 gauge in various weights and barrel lengths.

Bergmann

Bergmann's first pistol patent was taken out in 1892 in conjunction with Otto Brauswetter, a watchmaker from Szeged, Hungary. This covered the revolver-lock trigger, hammer mechanism, and clip-loading magazine, which later became standard features of Bergmann designs.

The first Bergmann pistol to achieve any success was a blowback model patented in 1893. This used a fixed barrel with an extension in which a rectangular bolt reciprocated. An external hammer acted on a firing pin inside the bolt, and feed was by a box magazine ahead of the trigger guard, which was loaded with a clip of five cartridges. An unusual feature was that the cartridges, in 5mm caliber, had no form of rim for extraction. Ejection from the chamber was the result of residual gas pressure, and the case was bounced out of the feedway upon striking the next round in the magazine.

This was replaced in 1897 by a conventional rimless cartridge with a groove for the extractor. These models were eventually produced in 5mm, 6.5mm, and 8mm calibers.

In 1901 a locked-breech pistol which used a laterally sliding locking piece to secure the bolt during firing was developed. It was chambered for a new 9mm cartridge of Bergmann design, and was offered for sale as the Mars; it was accepted for service with the Spanish Army in 1905.

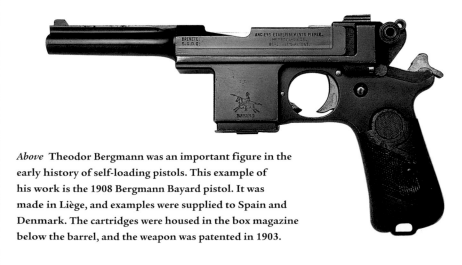

Above **Theodor Bergmann was an important figure in the early history of self-loading pistols. This example of his work is the 1908 Bergmann Bayard pistol. It was made in Liège, and examples were supplied to Spain and Denmark. The cartridges were housed in the box magazine below the barrel, and the weapon was patented in 1903.**

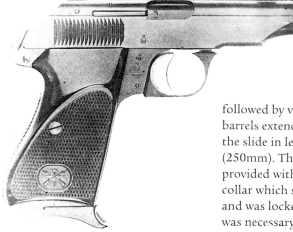

Above **A typical Bernadelli pocket pistol, the 7.65mm Standard model.**

Bernadelli

Bernadelli revolvers are generally based on Smith & Wesson practice, using solid frames with side-swinging cylinders locked by the ejector rod fitting into a lug beneath the barrel. The first models appeared in about 1950, in .22in and .32in chambering; later models appeared in 1958.

The automatic pistols began in 1945 with the Vest Pocket model, a tiny 6.35mm weapon with strong similarities to the Walther Model 9. This was then scaled up, in 1947, to produce the Pocket Model in 7.65mm caliber. This was originally produced with an 3.4in (85mm) barrel having an enveloping slide, but it was

followed by various models with the barrels extended beyond the front of the slide in lengths up to 10 inches (250mm). These barrels were provided with foresights built on to a collar which slipped over the muzzle and was locked there by a screw; this was necessary in order that the sight be removed to allow the slide to slip over the muzzle when dismantling the pistol.

In 1949 the first of a number of .22in pistols appeared, known as the Baby models. This was, in effect, no more than the 1945 Vest Pocket model modified so as to take the rimfire cartridge. The Standard model, also introduced in 1949, was similarly the Pocket model modified for .22in ammunition.

In 1950 the VB appeared; chambered for 9mm Browning Long or 9mm Parabellum. Since this is a blowback weapon, the 9mm Parabellum loading is a little powerful for it and, because the recoil spring has to be very powerful to cope with the heavy loading, it is too strong for reliable functioning with the weaker cartridge.

Above **The French Army Mousqueton d'Artillerie Mle 1892, a typical Berthier bolt-action design.**

Berthier

General A.V.P.M Berthier was a French Army officer who was responsible for two significant firearms designs, the Berthier rifle and the Vickers-Berthier machine gun. The former was a bolt-action rifle of conventional form which used a Mannlicher-type clip for loading to a box magazine below the action. The earlier Lebel rifle had used a tubular magazine below the barrel, which was slow to load, and so the Berthier design was adopted in order to keep abreast of clip-loading weapons introduced in other countries.

The first such weapon was the Cavalry Carbine M1890, which was followed by minor variations such as the Carabine de Gendarmerie, and the Mousqueton d'Artillerie. The first full-length rifle on the Berthier system was the Fusil des Tirailleurs Indo-Chinois Modele 1902, which

was again followed by small variants for different forces.

In 1915 the French Army expressed a preference for the Berthier design over the original Lebel. Large numbers of the Colonial Model 1907 rifle were removed from their Colonial owners and issued to the French Army in France, being called the Fusil Mle 07/15. But the prime drawback of the Berthier design was that the clip only carried three rounds; by comparison, the German Mauser held five, and the British Lee-Enfield ten.

Therefore in 1916 the design was modified, and a new five-round clip issued a change which necessitated placing a short sheet-metal extension on the bottom of the magazine. A number of them were again modified in 1934 to accept the new 7.5mm cartridge, which replaced the 8mm Lebel round.

Left **1889 model of the Italian Bodeo revolver.**

Bodeo

The Bodeo revolver was adopted as the Italian service sidearm in 1889 and remained in employment until its replacement in 1910 by the Glisenti. It was of standard design for its period, being a solid frame pistol with double-action lock, gate loading, and rod ejection. It was chambered for a 10.4mm cartridge. On opening the loading gate, the hammer was locked in a safe position. The mechanism was based on the patents of Abadie and little else of the design was original.

The only unusual feature is a hammer block which prevents the hammer falling far enough to strike the cartridge unless the trigger is pulled fully back. It is this item which caused the pistol to first be called Bodeo, since Sgr. Bodeo was at the head of the commission which drew up the specification, and furthermore is believed to have been responsible for this device.

The pistol appeared in two forms: one had an octagonal barrel, a folding trigger, and no trigger guard; the other had a cylindrical barrel and a normal trigger and guard. The former was for troops, the latter for NCOs and officers. Both patterns were produced at the same time, in numerous factories, and are marked accordingly. In the past the fixed-trigger model has been called the Model 1894.

Borchardt

This was an automatic pistol invented by Hugo Borchardt, and patented in September 1893. The action of the Borchardt pistol relied upon the Maxim toggle lock in modified form. The toggle relies upon the fact that when laid flat, with the central joint below the line of thrust and braced against the pistol frame, it forms a solid strut behind the exploding cartridge and thus securely locks the breech.

In the Borchardt action, the toggle unit was broken by the action of the barrel and locked toggle recoiling together across the frame of the pistol until the rear end of the toggle, carrying a roller, striking a curved surface and then deflected downwards. This caused the other end of that toggle arm to rise, and thus break the joint. At this point the pressure on the base of the cartridge could force open the breech, causing the toggle to rise still further and place tension on a spring. The stored energy of the spring later closed the

toggle, forcing a cartridge out of the magazine and into the chamber as the toggle was once more straightened out and locked.

The greatest difficulty lay in developing a suitable cartridge to work with this action, and Borchardt developed a bottle-necked rimless case with a 7.65mm jacketed bullet.

The Borchardt was generally provided with a wooden butt-stock which could be clamped to the rear of the frame to convert the pistol into a species of self-loading carbine. With a barrel length of 7.5inches, this was a feasible idea, albeit somewhat weakened by the absence of any form of adjustable rear sight.

Boys

This British antitank rifle was named after Captain H. C. Boys, head of the design team which developed the rifle, and who died a few days before the rifle was approved for service in November 1937. It was a bolt-action rifle in .55in caliber which used a belted cartridge case. The rifle was

Above **The Borchardt M93, the first automatic pistol to sell in quantity.**

five feet long, weighed 36 lbs, propelled its bullet at 3250 ft/sec, and could penetrate armor at 30 yards range. A five-round magazine was mounted above the action, and the barrel was permitted to recoil in the gun frame; a muzzle brake was fitted and the butt was heavily cushioned, all measures to try to mitigate the recoil force. In spite of this, though, it was still a fearsome weapon to fire.

In 1940 a tungsten-cored bullet was developed, and in 1942, a shortened model was briefly tried. But the antitank rifle had, by 1941, outlived its usefulness. Once the lightweight projectors for hollow charge bombs appeared, the Boys, like other anti-tank rifles, rapidly disappeared from service.

Brigadier

This name has been applied to two distinct pistol designs. The first, manufactured in 1950 by the North American Arms Company (NAACO) of Toronto, Canada, was a copy of the Browning GP35 automatic. It was generally larger than the Browning, had a light alloy frame, a removable trigger mechanism module, and a safety catch on the slide, which physically blocked the movement of the firing pin. It was chambered for a .45in cartridge of greater power than the usual .45in

Above **The comparative lightness of the .55in Boys rifle meant that it could be easily moved by one man. Surviving examples of this short-lived antitank rifle are popular with American and British target shooters as well as military reenactment groups.**

ACP round, which developed a muzzle velocity of 1600 ft/sec. With suitable modification, the pistol could be converted into the submachine gun known as the Borealis. The development never got beyond the prototype stage, as there was no military interest in the design.

The second Brigadier pistol was the Beretta M951 military pistol in 9mm Parabellum caliber.

Browning

John Moses Browning was America's, and one of the world's, foremost firearms inventors. He is reputed to have built his first rifle while he was still a boy, and his first patent, for a breech-loader, was obtained when he was 24 years old. His expertise covered all types of weapons, from pocket pistols to anti-aircraft artillery. Weapons to his design were manufactured by Remington, Winchester, Colt, and the Fabrique National d'Armes de Guerre of Herstal, Liège, Belgium, the products of this latter company being the only ones to carry the Browning name.

Browning was responsible for two basic pistol designs, a pocket blowback and a military locked-breech automatic. The former and a variant of the latter were produced by FN of Liège in the following models:

Browning 1900: Also called the Old Model, this was a 7.62mm blowback automatic that used a recoil spring mounted in the slide above the barrel, and had the recoil spring act also as the mainspring for the firing pin.

Browning 1903: This was originally produced in 9mm Browning Long caliber. This pistol used a new method of construction in which the barrel was attached to the pistol frame by ribs beneath the chamber; this allowed the pistol to be dismantled very easily by pulling back the slide and rotating the barrel to free the ribs. The system was so simple that it attracted

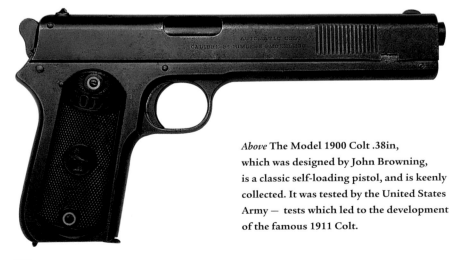

Above **The Model 1900 Colt .38in, which was designed by John Browning, is a classic self-loading pistol, and is keenly collected. It was tested by the United States Army — tests which led to the development of the famous 1911 Colt.**

Above A Browning 9mm GP35 pistol, also known as HiPower. This weapon was originally produced in Belgium, but during its occupation in World War II, a number were made in Canada by John Inglis of Toronto. On this example the original black plastic grips have been replaced by molded rubber grips for more comfortable shooting.

innumerable copyists, particularly in Spain.

Browning 1906: This was a smaller, 6.35mm version, of the 1903 model.

Baby Browning: This was the sales name for two 6.35mm automatic pistols manufactured by the Fabrique National d'Armes de Guerre (FN) of Herstal, Liège, Belgium, to the patents of John M. Browning. The first was introduced in 1906 and was called the Browning Baby model in early sales literature, though the name was later dropped. This pistol is more generally known simply as the Model 1906. It was a simple blowback pistol weighing 13 oz with a six-shot magazine, and it was provided with grip and magazine safety devices. A manual safety catch was later added, the model then being advertised as the Triple Sûreté model.

The second model, known from its inception as the Baby Browning, is similar in general design but smaller in all dimensions, having been introduced in the early 1920s in order to meet the demand for very small pocket pistols, and also to counter the competition from other small models such as the Menz Liliput. It weighed 10 oz, retained the six-shot magazine, but did not have the grip safety. The outline was generally more

square and compact than that of the 1906 model.

Browning 1910: This model had a complete change of design. This 7.65mm pistol had the return spring arranged around the barrel and had the slide shaped in a roughly tubular form. Browning 1922 was the 1910 with lengthened slide and barrel.

Browning GP35: The Grand Puissance 1935 was a locked-breech military pistol, development of which began immediately after World War I. It was patented in 1927, the year after Browning's death, and was introduced in 1935.

The GP35 uses Browning's system of locking breech to slide by ribs on the top of the barrel, which then engage into cuts in the undersurface of the slide. Barrel and slide thus have to recoil locked together. A forged lug under the barrel has a shaped cutout which engages with a cross pin in the pistol frame, and the action of the shaped cutout on the pin is such that the rear of the barrel is pulled down after a short recoil, thus freeing the

Above **The Browning 1878 rifle is based on John Browning's original falling block patent of 1887.**

lugs from their grooves. This unlocks the breech, and the barrel is held while the slide is free to recoil and complete the unloading-loading cycle. This use of a forged lug beneath the barrel in place of Browning's original swinging link has been widely copied, notably in the designs of Petter, SIG, and in the Polish VIS-35 pistol.

The Browning pistols which do not carry his name are made by the Colt company.

Browning's Automatic Rifle could fire single or automatic shots. In its original conception, the soldier would carry it at his hip, on a sling, firing it as he advanced across No Man's Land. This idea was later abandoned and it came to be used as a light machine gun, being adopted in post-war years by Belgium, Sweden, and other European countries. Nevertheless, it was not well suited for this role since it lacked an interchangeable barrel and the 20-shot bottom-mounted magazine was inconvenient when the weapon was being fired from the prone position. The United States Army retained it as their squad automatic until after the Korean War.

In the sporting field, Browning developed a self-loading .351in rifle which was made in the United States in 1906 by Remington as their Model 8. It was also made for European sale by FN of Liège. This was a blowback weapon, and it remained in production for many years. A .22in version was later made, first by FN in 1914, and later by Remington as their Model 16.

Browning patented his first automatic shotgun in 1900, which was placed on the market by FN. This was a long recoil weapon in which the barrel and breech recoiled together a distance greater than the length of a cartridge, at the end of which stroke the breech was unlocked and held while the barrel returned. Once the barrel was back in the forward position, the breech lock was released and loaded the next round from a five-shot tubular magazine.

Other shotguns bear the Browning name: an over-and-under double gun introduced in 1931, a short-recoil automatic of 1954, a single gun of 1970, and a gas-operated automatic introduced in 1974, but these were not from John Browning's drawing board. The family name was continued by Browning's son Valentine (who designed the short-recoil gun) and the Browning Arms Company of Arnold, Missouri now manufacture and market Browning weapons in the United States.

Right **The model shown here is a Browning F-N Model 1906, vest pocket, six-shot, .635mm pistol. It has a grip safety catch. It was probably intended as a self-defense weapon because the caliber is small and the 2 inch barrel can hardly have been appropriate for shooting at any great distance. It was produced in very large quantities.**

Above **The 5.56mm CAL rifle.**

CAL automatic

Carbine Automatique Légère was a light assault rifle developed by the Fabrique National d'Armes de Guerre of Herstal, Belgium. It is a 5.56mm caliber weapon and has a gas cylinder above the barrel. A piston in this cylinder is driven back on firing, and the piston rod strikes a bolt carrier and then returns to its original position in the cylinder. This brief impulse given to the bolt carrier is sufficient to drive the carrier backward against the resistance of a return spring. As the carrier moves, a cam track cut in its top and side engages with a lug on the bolt and revolves the bolt to unlock it from the barrel; once the bolt is unlocked it is carried back by the bolt carrier and then returned by spring action. As it returns it picks up a fresh cartridge from the 20-shot bottom-mounted magazine and loads it into the chamber, after which the continued forward movement of the bolt carrier turns and locks the bolt once more.

In addition to permitting single shots or automatic fire, the mechanism on early models contained a burst fire selector which allowed three shots to be fired for a single pressure on the trigger.

Campo-Giro automatic

This was a Spanish service pistol adopted in January 1914. It was invented and patented by Lt. Col. Venancio Lopez de Ceballos y Aguirre, Count of Campo Giro, between 1900 and 1904. The prototypes were made by the Fabrica de Armas de Oviedo in 7.65mm Parabellum and 9mm calibers.

An improved model was then developed and chambered for the standard Spanish service pistol round, the 9mm Largo or Bergmann-Bayard. This became known as the 1910 Model. So far the Campo-Giro had been a locked-breech weapon with a laterally sliding bolt lock beneath the chamber, but after Army tests, several modifications were

made to the design, the most important being the removal of the breech locking system so as to turn the pistol into a simple blowback type. Operation was controlled by an exceptionally strong return spring, together with shock absorbers in the frame to buffer the powerful recoil arising from the heavy cartridge.

A slightly modified version, whose changes lay mainly in the functioning of the safety catch, was later introduced as the Model 13/16. After World War I, its designation was changed to Model 1921.

Cei-Rigotti

Captain Amerigo Cei-Rigotti of the Italian Army invented this self-loading rifle in 1895. He demonstrated it at Brescia in 1900, revealing it to be gas-operated by a piston beneath the barrel which acted, through a cam, to rotate and unlock the bolt. It was chambered for the Italian service 6.5mm cartridge, and fed from a clip-loaded magazine beneath the action; various sizes of magazine, tip to 50 rounds capacity, were provided. During the demonstration Cei-Rigotti fired the weapon as an automatic, discharging 15 shots in one second, and also showed that by operating a selector, it could fire single shots.

The actual rifle, one of the very few surviving specimens, is today in the Museum of the School of Infantry. No military interest could be aroused in the design, and as a result, no production took place.

Right **The model 1913/16 Campo-Giro automatic was standard Spanish Army issue until 1921.**

Champion

This is a single-shot target pistol with a hinged drop-down barrel and exposed hammer, designed by the Koucky brothers and manufactured by Zbrojovka Brno company, former Czechoslovakia. Also called the ZKP-493, it is popular with competition shooters in Central Europe.

Charola y Anitua

One of the earliest automatic pistols, the Charola y Anitua appeared in 1897, manufactured by Garate, Anitua y Cia of Eibar, Spain. The butt and trigger are based on contemporary revolver practice, with an external hammer, but the rest of the design is reminiscent of Bergmann or Mauser designs and may have been inspired by them. The Charola had the distinction of being the smallest caliber pistol ever to employ a positively locked breech; it fires a tiny 5mm bottle-necked cartridge of low power and breech locking is quite superfluous. The breech lock was a swinging wedge pinned to the pistol frame and entering a recess in the bolt.

Chicago protector

This was the Turbiaux palm-squeezer pistol as manufactured under license by the Chicago Fire Arms Company in 1892 to 1895.

The American licensee for the Turbiaux was originally the Minneapolis Fire Arms Company, and they made and sold a .32in seven-shot model in the late 1880s. A salesman of this company called Peter H. Finnegan considered that the design could be improved; and together with a partner named Corrigan, set up the Chicago Fire Arms Company and purchased the license to the Turbiaux patent. He then negotiated with the Ames Sword Company of Chicopee Falls, Massachusetts, to make 25,000 pistols to his improved design. The Ames Company employed a man named Crouch to set up production, and Crouch, together with Finnegan, perfected some small improvements

Right **This curious looking weapon is a squeeze or palm pistol. It was designed to be held in the clenched fist, with the barrel projecting between the fingers. To fire a shot, the fist was clenched, which squeezed in the curved bar (the trigger) at the rear.**

which Finnegan patented in 1893. These improvements were a matter of more robust general construction and a grip safety device.

Chinese weapons

The Type 64 Silenced Pistol was an unusual weapon, which appears to have little purpose other than as an assassination weapon. The Type 64 is a blowback 7.65mm pistol with an integral silencer of high efficiency. The 7.65mm cartridge is of rimless type and is unique to this pistol; while apparently similar to the common 7.65mm ACP cartridge, it is of slightly different dimensions and not semi-rimmed. A refinement of the pistol's design is the ability to lock the slide to the barrel so that it cannot recoil in the usual blowback way and the pistol thus becomes, in effect, a single-shot weapon. Locking the pistol in this fashion ensures that there is no mechanical noise or ejected case to betray the firer. Where this is of less importance, the slide is unlocked and the pistol functions as a self-loader.

The Type 68 rifle is a Chinese amalgam of two Russian designs; in outline it appears to be based on the Simonov SKS carbine, but the gas-operated mechanism uses a rotating

Above **The Charola y Anitua automatic pistol in 5mm caliber.**

bolt in a carrier, based on the Kalashnikov AK47 rifle. It fires the Soviet 7.62mm X 39 short cartridge from a 15-round box magazine and can be used for single shots or automatic fire.

Chylewski's

Witold Chylewski designed an automatic pistol which could be operated entirely by one hand. It had a slide retracting lever which formed the front edge of the trigger guard; by gripping the pistol in the normal way, the forefinger could be placed around this lever and squeezed, which drew back the slide to cock and load. After releasing the lever, the finger could be transferred to the trigger, and for subsequent shots the slide retracting lever did not move.

About 1000 pistols are reputed to have been made for Chylewski by the Société Industrielle Suisse.

Colt

Samuel Colt set up his Patent Fire
Arms Manufacturing Company in
Paterson, New Jersey, in 1836 and
began making pistols, rifles,
shotguns, and carbines, all of which
were based on the revolving principle.
But due to slow sales, in 1843 the
company closed.

Below **One of the most powerful cap-and-
ball revolvers ever made was the 1847
Walker Colt. Only 1,100 originals were
produced, but many working replicas like
the Italian Uberti are still made in Europe.
The muzzle loading cap-and-ball revolver
does not use cartridges; black powder
propellant is poured in the chambers and a
round ball or conical bullet is rammed on
top. Ignition is provided by the percussion
cap on the nipple at the closed end of the
chamber, which blasts a flame into the
chamber when hit by the hammer.**

In 1847, however, the Mexican
War stimulated demand for firearms,
and General Zachary Taylor,
impressed with the Colt revolvers
owned by some of his officers,
dispatched a Captain Sam Walker to
see Colt and arrange for the
production of a military revolver.
Walker suggested certain
improvements, Colt produced a
design, and in January 1847 was given
an order for 1,000 pistols. Having no
factory, he subcontracted the order to
Eli Whitney, a noted Massachusetts
manufacturer of arms and inventor
of the cotton gin. A second order for
another 1000 pistols was given in
November 1847, and from the
proceeds of these orders Colt was able
to open another factory of his own.
From then on, he occupied himself
primarily with traveling and
promoting his designs worldwide.

Left **Because the Colt Bisley Flattop was intended for target shooting, the sight — a tall, blade front sight — is far more prominent.**

In 1849, just as his new factory was ready, the California Gold Rush began, the drive to open up the West followed, and every prospector and adventurer outfitted himself with Colt's weapons. In 1851 he went to London to exhibit his arms at the Great Exhibition, arousing considerable interest and eventually persuading the British Army and Royal Navy to buy several thousand revolvers. In 1853 his London Armory was opened; largely because the American factory was unable to produce weapons fast enough to meet domestic and foreign demands. In 1855 he opened a new large factory at Hartford, Connecticut, a plant capable of volume production sufficient to meet any demand. The following year he closed down his London factory.

Subsequent to Colt's untimely death at the age of 47, the company was run by a succession of directors who were sufficiently astute to keep the company prosperous, though they exhibited, at times, a surprising reluctance to adopt new ideas or abandon old ones, which led to some dubious designs and outdated models. Nevertheless, the quality and reliability of Colt arms, particularly pistols, carried the firm across the odd rough patch.

Colt's first product was the Paterson revolver, of .34in caliber with a five-shot cylinder. It was, of course, a percussion weapon, with nipples recessed into the back of the cylinder, which was mounted on a central arbor. The 51 inch octagonal barrel was forged with a lug which passed over the front end of the arbor and which was located firmly on the front end of the pistol frame. It was then locked in place by a cross pin which passed through slots in the barrel lug and the arbor. Since the top of the cylinder was thus exposed,

this form of construction has given rise to the term "open frame." A thumb-cocked hammer was fitted, and a folding trigger without a guard, which automatically unfolded as the hammer was cocked. To load, the pistol had to be dismantled by removing the cross pin and the cylinder. The pistol was therefore sold with a spare cylinder which could be carried ready loaded and quickly substituted for a fired cylinder. In 1839 Colt patented a lever-rammer which was fitted beneath the barrel, allowing the cylinder chambers to be loaded in the pistol.

Above **The long-lasting Colt .45in self-loading pistol has served the United States armed forces well. First introduced in 1911 (right), it was modified in 1921, the most obvious change being the curved extension at the bottom of the back of the butt. At this time it became the 1911A1.**

The rifles and shoulder arms produced by Colt used the same basic mechanism: in effect, they were revolving pistols but with long barrels and a stock suited to firing from the shoulder. By and large, these were less popular than the pistols. It is said that, due to the larger charges used in the rifles and shotguns, there was a greater tendency for "flash-over," the flame from the exploding charge leaking past the cylinder/barrel joint and igniting the charges in the other chambers, generally to the detriment of the firer's forward hand.

The order for pistols for the Mexican War led to the Walker or Whitneyville model. This used the same form of construction but with a conventional trigger and guard. Intended for military use it was much larger and more powerful than the Paterson, being of .44in caliber with a 9 inch barrel and six-shot cylinder and weighing over 41 lbs.

Subsequent percussion models — the Dragoon and Pocket models of 1848, the 1851 Navy, 1860 Army, and 1862 Police, were little more than variations on the same open-frame design. The only notable change in design was due to Elisha Root, Colt's factory manager, who developed a solid frame revolver with side-mounted hammer, sold as the New Model Pocket Pistol from 1855.

Also in 1855, Rollin White obtained his patent for "cylinders bored end to end" to allow breech loading. This patent was acquired by the Smith & Wesson company. As soon as Colt's master patent expired in 1857, Smith & Wesson went into production with a breech-loading cartridge revolver which, in turn, gave

them a master patent allowing them to effectively stifle competition.

Fortunately for Colt, ballistic development was in its early days, and those first metallic cartridges were relatively weak, allowing the percussion revolver, with its ability to handle powerful charges and heavy bullets, to survive for several more years. In an endeavor to emulate the rapid-loading facility of the breech-loading pistol, Colt developed a special cylinder which accepted a metallic cartridge inserted from the front of the chamber, the

assembly being called the Thuer Conversion. This allowed rapid loading without the need to have the chambers bored through.

In 1873, the company introduced the New Model Army, Frontier, or Peacemaker, as it is variously called. This was a solid-frame, rod-ejecting, six-shot revolver in .45in caliber which, in spite of minor flaws, rapidly gained a reputation for reliability in adverse conditions and became the Western revolver. Accepted after rigorous testing by the United States Army in 1873, the Frontier was subsequently manufactured in almost every practical caliber from .22 to .476in, and remained in production without a break until 1940 by which time over 357,000 had been made. In 1955 production was resumed in order to meet public demand.

Below **The Colt Match Target .22in pistol is a top-quality target weapon. It has a heavy barrel, which is long to give good velocity and long sight radius. The further apart the front and rear sights are set, the easier it is to get a good sight picture and so reduce errors resulting from misalignment. The shaped grip allows the gun to be held firmly.**

The Frontier was a single action pistol; to satisfy demands for a double action weapon, the Lightning model was offered in 1877. Based broadly on the Frontier model, it turned out to be less successful, largely due to a complicated lock mechanism which soon broke and was virtually unrepairable.

This pistol was replaced, to some extent, by the Double Action Army of 1878, though even this improved and stronger weapon failed to attract much enthusiasm.

In addition to heavy military revolvers, Colt also produced a wide selection of pocket pistols. Most notable among these was the Cloverleaf series, which gained its popular name from the deeply indented four-shot cylinders of the first models, a configuration selected to allow the cylinder to be part-

Above **Produced from 1871 until 1876, the Colt House pistol preceded the Single Action Army Revolver in the development of metallic cartridge revolvers. Because of the shape of the cylinder, the four-shot version was known as the Cloverleaf model. Several versions were made in .41in long or short rimfire.**

turned and present a thinner bulk for carrying in the pocket.

Colt's next major step was the introduction of a solid-framed revolver with the cylinder mounted on a crane arm, allowing it to be swung sideways from the frame for ejection and reloading. This first appeared on the Navy Model of 1889, which adopted this name when the United States Navy bought 5000 of them. This model became the pattern for subsequent designs, and apart from the Frontier model, all Colt revolvers since that time have used the solid-frame configuration, in conjunction with minor improvements in the method of retaining, locking, or revolving the cylinder.

Colt's last important innovation was their introduction of the Positive Safety Lock, an addition to the trigger mechanism which positively blocked the falling hammer unless the trigger was correctly pulled back. This prevented accidental firing such as could occur if the hammer were let slip during thumb cocking, or if the pistol was dropped so as to land upon the hammer.

When the automatic pistol began to appear in Europe in the 1890s, Colt was one of the few American companies to take note, quickly realizing that if a reliable pistol could be produced, they could establish a lead in that field as commanding as the one they made in the revolver field. They achieved their aim, and have sustained their lead ever since.

As with revolvers, the company set out from the start to produce a weapon acceptable to the military, submitting their first design for test in 1898. This used the Browning-patented swinging link system of breech locking, in which the barrel was attached to the pistol frame by two hinged links located at the breech and at the muzzle. The upper surface of the barrel carried two lugs which, when the pistol was at rest, engaged in two grooves in the interior of the slide. On firing, recoil made the barrel move back; due to the engagement of lugs and grooves, the slide — which formed the breech block — also moved back so that the breech was held securely closed. Due to the links, continued movement of the barrel carried it downward, still parallel with the frame, and disengaged the lugs so that the breech was free to open and the slide to recoil.

The first pistol to be marketed, the Model 1900, was chambered for a .38in rimless cartridge of considerable power. The United States Army and Navy bought some 250 for trial, while others were sold commercially. Changes were then made as experience showed the need; in 1905 the United States Army came firmly to the decision that nothing less than a .45in caliber would be

Right **The open cylinder of a Colt Python .357in Magnum revolver. The famous trademark, a small horse, can be seen on the frame.**

acceptable as a military sidearm. Colt developed a new .45in rimless cartridge and a suitable design of pistol. In 1907 an exhaustive test by the Army found the Colt design worthy of further development, and eventually the Model 1911 was accepted by the Army as their service pistol.

While military considerations were of prime importance, Colt did not neglect the civilian market for the automatic pistol of lesser power, and produced a number of simple and reliable pocket blowback pistols which were also based on Browning patents. Their Model 1903 was essentially the same as the Browning 1903. In a similar manner the Colt .25in model 1908 was the same as the Browning 1906.

Another well-known Colt automatic pistol series is the Woodsman .22in hunting and target model.

After World War II Colt acquired the rights to the Armalite rifle designed by Eugene Stoner, and from this design, with Stoner as consultant, developed their own CAR (Colt Automatic Rifle) series.

Dardick

The basic idea of this pistol was conceived by David Dardick in 1949. The weapon is in the form of a revolver, but instead of the conventional cylinder there is a star wheel with three triangular cut-outs in place of chambers. The magazine is in the pistol butt, and spring power forced the top round from the magazine into one of the star wheel cut-outs. Pressure on the trigger revolved the star wheel to align the cartridge with the pistol barrel and then dropped the hammer to fire it in the usual manner. The novelty of this design lay in the fact that the cartridge was not contained in a conventional chamber but in an open chamber, two sides of which were formed by the cut-out in the star wheel, and the third side by the top strap of the revolver frame. The next pull on the trigger revolved the star

wheel again, bringing up the next cartridge from the magazine and also carrying the spent case around and ejecting it through a port on the right side of the pistol.

Due to the triangular shape of the cut-out, the cartridge case had to be triangular and capable of withstanding much more pressure than normal. These ends were achieved in the first models by forming the cases of extruded triangular aluminum section, but later cartridges were made of polycarbonate plastic.

Darne shotgun

The brothers Regis and Pierre Darne, after some years of work as gunsmiths, perfected their unique shotgun in 1895. Instead of the usual drop-down form of double-barreled gun, the barrels are rigidly attached to the frame and the breech unit is withdrawn to the rear by operating a lever in the center of the breech block. This opens the breech and extracts the empty case.

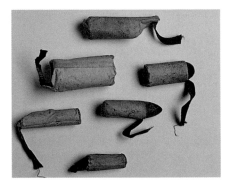

Left **These mid-nineteenth century paper cartridges were manufactured by Eley Brothers, the famous London ammunition firm. The smaller cartridges were for the .31in Pocket Colt percussion revolver, and others were made for the Adams .45in revolver.**

Left **A 38- bore Adams percussion revolver, dating from the mid-nineteenth century.**

released by a single pull on the plunger-type trigger. Relatively few appear to have been made as production ceased in 1914.

Deane and Adams

This is the name under which the percussion revolvers of Robert Adams were sold. These revolvers arose from Adams' partnership with John Deane and his son John Deane Jr. The firm displayed revolvers at the Great Exhibition of 1851, and the subsequent interest in these and in the exhibits of Colonel Colt led them to concentrate on pistol production. The pistol's acceptance by the British Army as the Deane and Adams Pistol set the seal of approval on it, and it was widely sold for several years.

Decker revolver

Wilhelm Decker of Zella St Blasii, Germany patented an unusual pocket revolver in 1912. It was a solid frame six-shot model in 6.35mm caliber, was hammerless, and used an axial firing pip which was cocked and

Deer gun

The deer gun was a 9mm caliber single-shot pistol and was probably fathered by the American CIA who intended to flood South East Asia with pistols during the Vietnam War. It was based on the same concept as the Liberator pistol of World War II, a simple weapon capable of being used by the uninstructed and capable of killing at short range.

To load, the barrel is unscrewed from the diecast frame, and a 9mm Parabellum cartridge placed into the chamber. The barrel is then screwed back into the frame. On pressing the trigger, a striker is cocked and released to fire the cartridge. The barrel is then unscrewed and the spent case ejected by poking it out with any convenient twig before loading. A supply of cartridges could be carried in the hollow butt.

Derringer

Deringer was the son of a German gunsmith who immigrated to America. In 1806 he set up his own shop in Philadelphia and made a variety of muzzle-loading rifles and pistols. In 1825 he produced a short, heavy caliber, single-shot pistol which could be easily concealed. This pistol attained great popularity, not to mention notoriety, after John Wilkes Booth used one to assassinate President Lincoln. He failed to patent his design, and it was therefore copied by many other makers, the term "Derringer" (note the different spelling) being loosely applied to any short-barreled single-shot pistol.

After his death, the name was continued in the Deringer Revolver and Pistol Co. until 1879, producing cheap .22, .32 and .38in rimfire

Below **The original Deringer pistols were single-shot defence pieces, but the name was later corrupted to "derringer" and applied to small multibarreled hand guns. The COP pistol has four fixed barrels and a rotating striker which fires each .357in Magnum cartridge in turn.**

revolvers on tip-up frames, loosely copied from the contemporary Smith & Wesson designs. The Colt company then acquired rights to the name and manufactured cartridge breech-loaders for several years under the Deringer name.

Dimancea

This revolver was made in small numbers by the Gatling Arms & Ammunition Co. of Birmingham. The novelty of this design lay in the extracting and firing arrangements. On releasing a latch, the barrel and cylinder could be swung sideways and then drawn forward, a fixed extractor plate then pulling the empty cartridge cases from the chambers. The firing mechanism, entirely concealed within the frame, was a sliding firing pin which was cocked

Above These small vest pocket double-barreled pistols are usually referred to as Derringers, and were produced by many of the big manufaturers. They were available in single and double barrel versions, and the usual caliber was .41in, although other calibers were also produced.

and released by a six-armed paddle wheel rotated by successive pulls of the trigger. Manufacture is believed to have taken place between 1886 and 1890, and specimens in .38 and .45in caliber are known.

Dreyse

Niklaus von Dreyse (1787–1867) was the inventor of the Needle Gun, the bolt action breech-loading rifle which introduced breech loading as a viable military system and which paved the way for every bolt action rifle. He founded the Waffenfabrik von Dreyse in 1841 to manufacture needle guns, revolvers on the needle gun principle, and percussion revolvers.

The company continued in the firearms business, even after the death of Dreyse, and eventually adopted the name Rheinmetall and later Rheinmetall-Borsig. The company has not used the Dreyse style on weapons made since 1918.

Dreyse weapons were actually designed by Louis Schmeisser, at that time in the company's employ, and the first pistol appeared in 1907. It was an unusual design; the slide was cranked, with the major portion lying on top of the fixed barrel, and the shorter section forming the breech block and lying behind the barrel, enclosed in a slab-sided casing at the rear of the frame. The recoil spring was located around the barrel, and linked to the slide. Pulling back the upper portion of the slide caused the breech block section to appear through a hole at the rear of the frame. Produced only in 7.65mm caliber, it continued to be made throughout the First World War, and many numbers were taken by the German Army as substitute standard weapons.

A 6.35mm pistol appeared next; this was of fairly conventional form, resembling the Browning 1906 in appearance, but not in construction. The third model was a 9mm pistol, an enlarged version of the 7.65mm type, but chambered for the 9mm Parabellum cartridge. Since the pistol was a blowback, this demanded a very strong return spring, and to cock the

Right **Drulov .22in target pistol.**

Right **The Dreyse 1.65mm pistol was introduced in 1907, and was carried by most second-line officers in the German Army during World War I. It was well made and had a magazine capacity of seven cartridges.**

pistol in the normal way by pulling back the slide, was extremely difficult. Schmeisser overcame this by fitting a rib on top of the slide, and linking the slide to the return spring. This rib could then be lifted, uncoupling the slide from the spring, and allowing the slide to be pulled back to cock and charge the pistol. With the slide returned to its forward position, the rib was pressed down to re-engage the slide and return spring for firing. Although this pistol was developed in 1911 for commercial sale, it was met with little success.

Drulov

A single-shot .22in pistol for competition shooting which was originally made by Druzstvo Lovena of Prague, this pistol is now made by the Dilo National-Cooperative of Svratovch, and distributed by the Omnipol export agency. Breech closure is accomplished by a rotating bolt operated by a knurled grip at its rear end; inside the bolt is the usual axial striker and spring. The barrel is 10in long and front and rear sights are fully adjustable. In spite of its export status, the Drulov is rarely seen outside Central Europe.

EM

Applied to a number of experimental weapons during the period 1940–1950, the initials of this rifle stand for Enfield Model. The most important models were as follows.

The EM1 was a self-loading rifle adopted by the British Army in 1945. It was gas operated and used a roller locking system similar to that later seen on the CETME rifle. The design was quite unusual, as the "bull-pup" configuration was adopted. In this layout, the bolt and breech are as far

Below **A lanyard fitted to the British Army Enfield revolver. The securing cords were supplied in the appropriate color of khaki for the Army, light blue for the Royal Air Force, and white for the Military Police.**

Right **This British service revolver is an Enfield No. 2 Mk1**. The main differences between this and earlier British service revolvers are that it was a smaller caliber — .38in rather than .45in — and it was self-cocking. The hammer lacked a spur, which made it impossible to pull back manually.**

back on the rifle as possible, close to the end of the butt, so that they are actually behind the firer's face when he takes aim. This allows the maximum barrel length to be accommodated within a given length of rifle and, in effect, allows the overall length of a rifle to be reduced without affecting the working length of the barrel. Other features which follow from this are the location of the magazine behind the pistol grip, and the need to raise the sight line well above the weapon to compensate for the straight-line layout. To avoid an easily damaged post foresight, the EM1 used a unity power optical sight contained in a permanently attached carrying handle above the barrel.

Steel pressings and plastic material were incorporated in the design in order to simplify production and reduce expense.

The EM2 was developed at the same time as the EM1, but by a different design team. It, too, was of the bull-pup type, and gas operated, but it used a less complicated breech locking system which resembled that of the Russian Degtyarev machine guns, two locking plates being forced sideways out of the bolt by the passage of the firing pin.

In 1951 it was announced that the EM2 would enter British service as the Rifle No. 9, but later in that year, after meetings of Defense Ministers of Britain, the United States, Canada,

Above The British Enfield .476in B.L. revolver was designed in 1879 and tested by various units of the British Army. After a somewhat mixed reception, it was modified slightly before being adopted as the official revolver in August 1880.

Above The extraction system of the Enfield revolver is remarkable. When the barrel catch was released and the barrel pushed downward, the cylinder moved forward, but a stationary plate retained the cases so that, eventually, there was sufficient room for the empty case to fall out.

and France, this decision was revoked and a fresh agreement to develop a new cartridge to become the NATO standard round was agreed. In 1957 the 7.62mm cartridge was adopted and attempts were made to adapt the EM2 design to this round, but they were not successful and the project was brought to an end.

Enfield/Lee-Enfield

This name was applied to various British military arms, derived from their inception or production at the Royal Small Arms Factory, Enfield Lock, Middlesex, which was founded in 1856.

The first weapon to bear the name was the Enfield Rifle Musket, Pattern 1852, a .577in muzzle-loading single-shot percussion rifle firing a Pritchett expanding bullet. The first rifle to be generally issued to British troops, and the last muzzle-loader, it was a highly successful weapon which gave good service in the latter part of the Crimean War as well as in India.

It was replaced by the Snider conversion, and then by the Martini-Henry breech-loaders, the Enfield name next appearing on an Enfield-Martini .402in rifle in 1886, which used Metford rifling. Though 70,000 such rifles were made, due to impending improvements, they were never issued.

In 1879, the factory produced drawings for a service revolver and had them approved. The prototypes were sent for trial in January 1880,

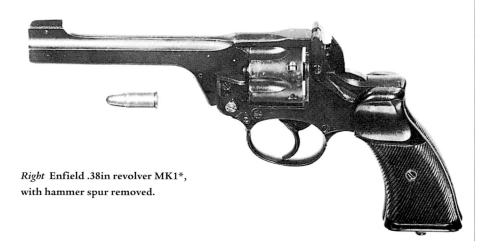

Right **Enfield .38in revolver MK1*, with hammer spur removed.**

Above **The Lee bolt action rifle.**

and the design was approved in August as the Pistol, Revolver, Breech-loading, Enfield Mark 1. It was a six-shot, hinged-frame revolver in .476in caliber, with an unusual extraction system; hinging the barrel down pulled the cylinder forward but left the extractor plate in place, in effect drawing the cylinder off the empty cases. As might be expected, the defect in this system was that the bottom case frequently failed to drop out of the frame.

Small improvements were soon required, and a Mark 2 pistol was issued in March 1882. The principal changes were the tapered-boring of the chambers to improve accuracy, and the installation of a hammer lock to prevent the pistol being accidentally fired while loading.

When the famed Lee-Enfield rifle ran into severe criticism during the early 1900s, Enfield developed a new rifle. This took the form of a .276in weapon using a Mauser-type bolt and

magazine, and an extremely powerful cartridge. It was not a success on its first trials, but development was hurriedly shelved at the outbreak of war in 1914. The grave shortage of rifles, however, led to the remodeling of the Pattern 1913 design in order to facilitate the standard .303in service cartridge. The new rifle (now called the Pattern 1914) was easier to mass-produce than the Lee-Enfield.

When the United States entered the war in 1917, it too was faced with a rifle shortage and, since the machinery for producing the Pattern 1914 was in existence in America, the United States authorities modified the design once more, this time to accept the United States Army's .30in cartridge. In this form the rifle was put into production as the Enfield Rifle M1917 or, in British nomenclature, the Pattern 17.

In post-World War I years the British Army elected to abandon the

.455in caliber for revolvers, and adopt a .38in instead. A design by Webley was turned down and an Enfield design adopted. In broad terms it was a copy of the Webley, but with some small modifications to the lockwork. This remained the service sidearm until the adoption of an automatic pistol in the 1950s.

The latest designs to emerge from Enfield are the 4.85mm Individual Weapon (rifle) and Light Support Weapon (light machine gun) which were announced in 1976. Both bear some resemblance to earlier EM designs, but have a much different mechanism as well as using a number of common components.

The Lee-Enfield rifle was introduced into British service in 1895 as the successor to the Lee-Metford. It was essentially the same weapon except that the rifling had been changed. The adoption of cordite propellant was found to be wearing out Lee-Metford barrels after as little as 4500 rounds had been fired through them, which lead to the subsequent adoption of a deeper form of rifling.

In all there were 24 rifles and two carbines in the Lee-Enfield series which were introduced between 1895 and 1949, but undoubtedly the most famous of these was the SMLE, or Rifle, Short, Magazine, Lee-Enfield

Above **A drawing of the Lee action; the bolt has just been opened. The simple trigger mechanism and the folded spring which forces the cartridge up, are seen here.**

introduced in 1903. This was developed as a short rifle to replace the long rifle used by infantry and the carbine used by cavalry and artillery. In addition, it had a deeper magazine to accommodate ten cartridges instead of five, and was arranged for faster loading by means of a charger of five cartridges. Although subjected to severe criticism by many self-styled experts of the day during World War I, the SMLE proved that it was probably the best all-round combat bolt action rifle ever made. The rear locking lugs of the bolt, while theoretically unsound and, if badly adjusted, conducive to inaccuracy, nevertheless allowed the bolt to be manipulated much faster and more easily than any other system, contributing to an aimed rate of fire in excess of 40 rounds a minute. The only real defect of this rifle was that it was a slow and intricate manufacturing proposition, and after 1918, various experimental models were made in order to settle on a design which retained the reliability and handiness of the SMLE, but which was better suited to mass production.

The result was Rifle No. 4 (the system of nomenclature had been changed in the 1920s), which appeared shortly after the outbreak of war in 1939, and became the standard British rifle. The visible changes to this rifle included the adoption of an aperture sight at the rear of the action instead of a U-sight in front of the chamber, and the exposure of about three inches of barrel in front of the wooden stock. The traditional sword-bayonet also vanished, in favor of a 9 inch spike. The Lee-Enfield was officially replaced as a standard rifle in 1957, but having been rebarreled to 7.62mm NATO caliber, is still in service as a sniping rifle.

ERMA

This acronym derived from the title Erfurter Maschinenwerke B. Giepel GmbH, a German company which originated in Erfurt after World War I.

The company is probably best-known for the series of submachine guns designed by Heinrich Vollmer and Berthold Giepel, and developed from about 1925 onward . The

ERMA - B. GEIPEL - GMBH
WAFFENFABRIK
ERFURT

Right **The Erma KGP-22 pistol, based on the lines of the Parabellum but with a simpler action.**

principal design feature was the collection of the bolt, firing pin, and return spring into a self contained unit enclosed within a telescoping tubular casing. This patented feature made assembly of the weapon very easy and also proofed the most vital parts against dust and dirt.

The Erma company also made ingenious conversion units comprising a special barrel and breech mechanism. These could be fitted into the standard army rifle and the Luger 08 pistol to permit their use with special 4mm caliber training ammunition. They then went on to manufacture a .22in automatic pistol for target shooting and then .22in rifles for sporting and competitive shooting, until 1939.

In postwar years the company returned to the submachine gun field in the late 1950s, producing a number of limited-production models for evaluation by the Bundeswehr. None were found suitable, and no more submachine gun designs have been produced since the early 1960s.

Instead, Erma reverted to the pistol field, and patented an ingenious variation of the Luger toggle lock, based on the mechanism used in pre-war training devices, and then incorporated this into a design of pistol based on the Luger. In fact, the breech is now no longer locked, but operates in the blowback mode whereby the lines of force on the toggle act to open it by spent case pressure alone. Since the introduction of the .22in caliber EP-

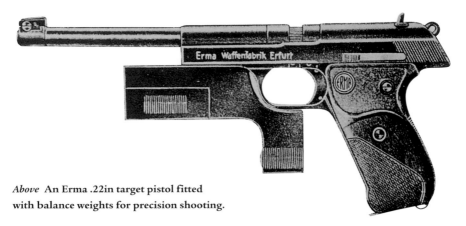

Above An Erma .22in target pistol fitted
with balance weights for precision shooting.

22 in 1964, other models in 7.65mm
and 9mm Short caliber have been
placed on sale. Production of all types
is understood to have reached some
70,000 within ten years.

Fabrique National

Fabrique National d'Armes de Guerre
(or FN) of Herstal, Belgium was
founded in 1889. It's SAFN (Semi-
Automatic, FN) rifle was designed by
Dieudonne Saive in 1940, with the
intention of providing the Belgian
Army with a new semiautomatic rifle.
It was gas operated, a cylinder above
the barrel carrying a short-stroke
piston which moved back only
enough to strike the bolt carrier and
impart movement. Thereafter the
impetus drove the carrier back, and
cam tracks inside it lifted the bolt out
of engagement with locking surfaces
in the gun body.

Although the SAFN achieved
considerable success, it did not
entirely satisfy Saive who, assisted by
Ernest Vervier, eventually produced a
fresh design, chambered for the new
7.62mm NATO cartridge. This
became the FAL-Fusil Automatique
Légère which was subsequently
adopted by armies internationally.
The FAL is gas operated, using a bolt
carrier with tipping bolt, much as the
SAFN. Various models with heavier
barrels, bipods, and facility for
automatic fire are used in the light
machine gun role.

With the growing popularity
of 5.56mm caliber assault rifles,
a new design based on the general
outline of the FAL and known as the
CAL (Carabine Automatique Légère)
was later developed.

The FN company has, of course,
manufactured all the various types

of Browning machine guns at one time or another, as well as producing the Browning Automatic Rifle in a number of variant styles to suit the requirements of different countries.

In the early 1950s Ernest Vervier developed the completely new MAG, (Mitrailleuse à Gaz) a gas operated, belt-fed weapon designed as a general purpose machine gun.

FG42

The Fallschirmgewehr 42 or FG42 was a selective-fire automatic rifle designed specifically for use by German airborne troops. Following the 1940 stated requirement, two companies, Rheinmetall and Krieghoff, produced prototypes.

The Rheinmetall design was accepted, but since that company could not find space for production, manufacture was done by Krieghoff.

The weapon was designed to be an automatic rifle which could also function as a light machine gun. It was gas operated, and fired the standard 7.92mm Mauser cartridge. The bolt was rotated to lock into the breech, and the firing mechanism was arranged so that for single shots the bolt was closed before the firing pin was struck, but in automatic fire the bolt was held open between bursts of fire so that the barrel and breech could cool down. This gave better accuracy for single-shot fire while reducing the chance of a "cook-off"

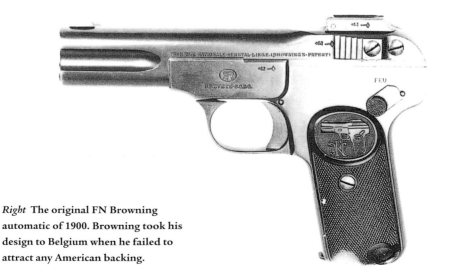

Right **The original FN Browning automatic of 1900. Browning took his design to Belgium when he failed to attract any American backing.**

after a burst of automatic fire. The gun was fed from a box magazine at the left side.

However, by the time the FG42 was perfected, German airborne troops were of less importance, and only about 7000 rifles were ever made. Nevertheless, it was an important step in the development of selective-fire rifles, and it achieved the feat of being a serviceable automatic rifle of light weight, yet firing an old-fashioned full-power cartridge.

Forehand & Wadsworth

This American company was operated by Sullivan Forehand and Charles Wadsworth. Their first products were a continuation of the .22in single-shot pistol, but later they turned to the manufacture of cheap solid-frame rimfire revolvers.

After 1888 they began production of hinged-frame revolvers in .32in and .38in center-fire calibers. These used a ribbed barrel and a spring catch above the standing breech to lock barrel and frame together, and in this respect they were similar to several contemporary designs from other makers. One solid-frame revolver in .44in caliber was named the Russian, which was an obvious attempt to emulate the successful Smith & Wesson .44in Russian; although the Forehand & Wadsworth

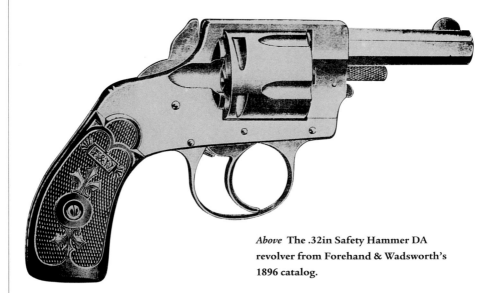

Above **The .32in Safety Hammer DA revolver from Forehand & Wadsworth's 1896 catalog.**

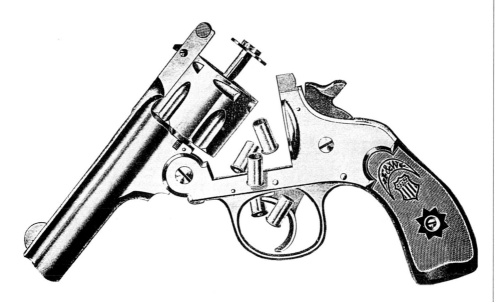

model had a superficial resemblance and was a much cheaper weapon.

French Ordinance

The first revolver to be adopted by the French services was a Lefaucheaux pinfire model, approved for issue in 1856 to the French Navy. Although only issued to the Navy, many Army officers acquired them, and with experience, this led to a demand for a similar Army revolver.

In 1873 an 11mm centre-fire Chamelot-Delvigne revolver was issued for cavalry troopers, followed in 1874 by a similar model, but with shorter barrel for general issue to officers. These were acquired from trade sources, and in 1886 the St.

Above **The Forehand & Wadsworth New Model .38in double action revolver with automatic extraction.**

Etienne arsenal began work on a design to replace the 1873 model so as to concentrate armament supply in government hands. The eventual result was the Model 1892, wrongly called the Lebel revolver, and more correctly known as the Model d'Ordonnance.

The Mle 92 was a solid-frame, robust and accurate weapon, with swing-out cylinder in 8mm caliber. A useful feature was the construction of the frame so that one side could be opened to allow access to the mechanism for repair and cleaning.

Frommer

Although he designed various military and sporting automatic rifles as well as some machine guns, Frommer is principally remembered for his automatic pistols. They were all far too complicated for what they did, and they are often criticized as being too delicate and prone to malfunction. However, this accusation is not borne out by their recorded usage as they would not have survived so long in military service had they not been reliable.

Frommer's first pistol, a long-recoil model using a rotating bolt, appeared in 1901. It was entered for various military trials and placed on sale, but it was a cumbersome article,

and was not a success. A modified, more compact version appeared in 1906. This version used the same mechanism, and chambered for a peculiar 7.65mm cartridge designed by Roth, instead of an even more peculiar 8mm from the same stable. In 1910 the design was changed to accept the standard 7.65mm ACP cartridge, but even so it sold in only small numbers, none of which are common today.

However, in 1912 he produced the Stop model. This model still used the long-recoil and rotating bolt system, but was a much more compact and reliable weapon chambered for the 7.65mm ACP cartridge. It was first adopted by the Austro-Hungarian

Above **The Frommer Model of 1901, an unsuccessful design.**

Above The Stop pistol of 1912 became
a prominent military pistol in spite
of its complicated action.

Above The Frommer Baby, which in spite
of its small size, still used the long recoil
locking system.

Army in 1912 and later by the Hungarian Army when it became a separate entity in 1919. The Stop model remained in service and police use until the end of World War II. It was also sold widely on the commercial market, a 9mm Short version being added in 1919.

At the same time that the Stop was introduced, a smaller model called the Baby appeared, which was still in 7.65mm caliber, and used the same method of actuation. The object here was the provision of a more pocketable weapon, and the Stop was seen primarily as a holster pistol.

In about 1921 Frommer introduced the Lilliput model, his first move away from the long recoil system and the use of locked breeches which, when all was said and done, were superfluous in the calibers he was using. The Lilliput was a 6.35mm simple blowback weapon, featuring an external hammer and grip safety, but using a fixed barrel and conventional type of slide. In 1929 an enlarged version in 7.65mm caliber was introduced simply as the Frommer M1929, and was immediately adopted by the Hungarian Army. It was robust and

Above **The M1929 of the Hungarian Army was a simple blowback pistol, derived from the Lilliput design.**

Above **The much simpler Frommer M1937 pistol adopted by the Hungarian Army; this version is in 7.65mm and was made for the German Luftwaffe.**

simple, and as a combat weapon was undoubtedly better than the Stop.

Finally, a year after Frommer's death, came the M1937, which was little more than a simplified and cleaned-up M1929, but in 9mm Short caliber. This was also adopted by the Hungarian Army, and during World War II, several thousand were made in 7.65mm caliber for the German Air Force.

Fusil F1

The Fusil F1 is a modern bolt-action magazine rifle used by the French Army as their sniper weapon. Produced by the Manufacture National d'Armes de St. Etienne, it is offered in three versions; Modèle A, the service weapon; Modèle B for competition shooting; and Modèle C for hunting. Modèle B and C are, of course, commercially available.

The difference between the three is primarily one of the attachments and accessories; Modèle A has a pistol grip, bipod, flash-hider, and image-intensifying sight, as befits a specialized military weapon. Modèle B has a more conventional stock and microadjustable target sights; while Modèle C has more ordinary iron sights plus a telescope sight, and can be had in chamberings other than the 7.62mm NATO or 7.5mm French service calibers.

Galand

Galand's basic revolver was an open frame, double-action arm in which a lever, lying beneath barrel and frame and usually forming the trigger-guard, operated the ejection system. By pressing down and forward on this lever, the barrel and cylinder were slid forward on the cylinder arbor. After a short travel, the extractor star plate was held, while the barrel and cylinder continued to move, so that the spent cases were withdrawn from the chambers and allowed to fall clear. From about 1868 onward, revolvers incorporating this system were produced in a wide variety of calibers.

The Velo-Dog revolver was a small-caliber pocket weapon which fired a special 5.5mm center-fire cartridge. Originally the pistol was an open-frame model with fixed trigger and guard, but this was soon replaced by a folding-trigger model; all were hammerless, as the hammer was concealed by a humped frame, so that there was no danger of the hammer catching on the pocket lining when being withdrawn.

The name Velo-Dog is said to be derived from "velocipede" and "dog," since the revolver was widely sold as a self-defense arm for cyclists in the 1890s. In those days, bicycle riders venturing into some of the more remote rural areas of Europe were liable to be attacked by dogs, and the Velo-Dog was the recommended self-defense antidote.

Galil

This was the service rifle of the Israeli Army, adopted in 1973. Designed by Israel Galili and Yakov Lior of Israeli Military Industries, it was first field-tested in 1969 and was introduced as the basic infantry weapon, intended to replace the existing semiautomatic rifle, the submachine gun, and the light machine gun in the squad automatic role.

The Galil is basically an assault rifle, but when fitted with a bipod, it can fill the light machine gun position. With a front pistol grip and short barrel, it can also be used as a submachine gun; and when fitted with a special launcher, it can be used to fire anti-tank and anti-personnel grenades. It fires the 5.56mm cartridge from 35- or 50-round magazines, and the standard version is provided with a folding metal butt, folding bipod, and carrying handle. There is also an SAR (Short Assault Rifle) version which has a short barrel and an optional front pistol grip. The Galil is gas operated, with a rotating bolt, and fires single shots, or at a rate of 650 rounds per minute.

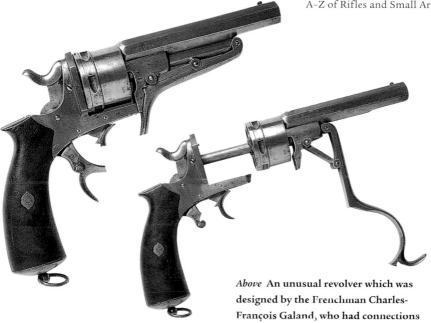

Above An unusual revolver which was designed by the Frenchman Charles-François Galand, who had connections in both Belgium and England. In 1868 he patented an extraction system.

Garand

The Garand rifle is a gas-operated rifle using a rotating bolt, chambered for the .276in cartridge developed by Pedersen. In 1929, after a severe competitive trial, Garand's rifle was selected for further development as the potential United States Army service rifle. By 1932 the design had been perfected, but General MacArthur, then Chief of Staff, opposed the adoption of the .276in cartridge on the grounds that the Army already had a vast investment in ammunition, and machinery for its production which they could not afford to waste.

Garand therefore redesigned his rifle to operate with the regulation .30in cartridge, and on 9th January 1936, his design was formally approved as the United States Rifle M1, thus becoming the first automatic rifle to be the standard infantry arm of a major army.

The Garand rifle uses a gas piston beneath the barrel to drive an operating rod which, by a cam arrangement, rotates and opens the bolt. It fires from an eight-round clip which is automatically ejected after the last shot of the clip has been fired, the bolt then being held back so that the rifle is ready for reloading.

Gaulois

This was the French "palm-squeezer" repeating pistol patented in 1893 by Mimard and Blachin, and manufactured by the Manufacture d'Armes et Cycles de St. Etienne. In 8mm caliber, and firing a special short cartridge, it consisted of a flat action body and short barrel with a squeeze grip at the rear end. Five bullets were placed in the box magazine inside the body, and the weapon was then gripped in the hand in order to squeeze in the rear grip. This chambered and fired a cartridge, and as the hand's squeeze was relaxed, a spring drove the grip out to eject the spent case and position the next cartridge for loading. It was originally marketed as the Mitrailleuse, but the name was changed in 1903.

Gewehr

The Gewehr 41 (M) was designed by Mauser, and used a muzzle cone to trap gas and thus force a piston rod backward. Movement of the rod was imparted to the rear portion of a two-piece bolt which, on moving backward, rotated the bolt head in order to unlock and then withdraw it. Both sections of the bolt were then thrust back by the piston to extract the spent case and, in returning, chamber a fresh round.

The Gewehr 41 (W) was made by Walther. This also used a muzzle trap, which deflected gas backward to drive an annular piston surrounding

Above **The Gaulois or Mitrailleuse pistol in 8mm caliber.**

Above **The 9mm Glisenti, with its cartridge.**

Below **The Italian Glisenti automatic pistol, showing the bolt in the fully recoiled position.**

the barrel. This, in turn, drove back an actuating rod to operate the bolt. Breech-locking was done by lugs forced sideways from the bolt by the passage of the firing pin, an adaptation of the Friberg-Kjellman system. Although this was, in truth, very little better than the Mauser design, it performed sufficiently well on test for it to be provisionally adopted for service. However, it was

later discovered that the muzzle trap and annular piston system were prone to jamming due to corrosion from powder fouling and from differential expansion of the barrel and piston, and its acceptance for service was canceled.

The Mauser Gewehr 98 and its variant models were the standard infantry rifles of the German Army from 1898 until 1945. It was a bolt-

action rifle with an integral five-round magazine; the bolt was locked by one rear and two forward lugs, and the striker was cocked by the opening movement of the bolt.

As a full-length infantry rifle, it originally fired the same 7.92mm cartridge that had been introduced with its predecessor, the M1888 Commission rifle. The Gewehr 98 was accompanied into service by a short version, the Karabiner 98, for use by mounted troops, artillery, and pioneers.

In the early 1900s, British and United States armies introduced short rifles — weapons which fell between the traditional long infantry rifle and the cavalry carbine, and which could be used as a universal army weapon. The German Army quickly adopted a short version of the Gewehr 98 in 1904. The barrel was shortened from 30 to 24 inches, and the bolt handle was turned down, instead of protruding at right angles from the action. This was formally adopted in 1908 as the Karabiner 98a, issues of which were first made to artillery and pioneer troops.

In 1903–1904, a new pointed bullet of slightly larger diameter was developed for the 7.92mm cartridge. Most early Gewehr 98s were modified by fitting new barrels, while Kar 98a models were designed for this new bullet from the outset.

After World War I the Gewehr 98 was modified by adopting the turned-down bolt handle, and making some small alterations in the sights, after which it was confusingly renamed the Karabiner 98b, despite the fact that it remained a full-length rifle. In 1934 a final design was drawn up, which amounted to little more than the Kar 98a, with slight changes to suit the manufacturer's convenience. This design was adopted as the Karabiner 98k (k for *kurz*, or "short") to become the standard rifle of the Wehrmacht.

Glisenti

Adopted in 1910 as the standard automatic pistol of the Italian Army, the Glisenti was a locked-breech pistol in 9mm caliber, the lock of which was a pivoting wedge in the frame. The 9mm cartridge was of the same dimensions as the 9mm

Above **The short rifle version of the Gewehr 98, known as the Karabiner 98k.**

Parabellum, but less powerfully loaded, a modification that probably occured due to the construction of the pistol.

The frame is open on the left side and covered with a plate, which means that the pistol lacks stiffness, a defect which more powerful ammunition would rapidly search out. The firing mechanism was unusual in that the pistol was reloaded by the recoil stroke of the bolt but not recocked; the striker was a self-cocking unit, tensioned and released by pulling the trigger. This has some appeal as a safety measure, since the pistol can hardly be fired accidentally, but it makes for a long and uncertain trigger pull due to the lack of accuracy in shooting.

Godsal

The Godsal rifle was an experimental model put forward for possible military adoption by Major P. T. Godsal, a retired infantry officer and target-shooting enthusiast who had frequently represented England at international shooting matches during the 1900s.

Godsal called his breech-locking system a "traveling block," but to the uninitiated it still looked like a bolt. It was, in fact, a two-piece bolt in which the small head carried the locking lugs and the handle, and rotated independently of the rest of the bolt which carried the firing pin. This positioning of the lugs gave the necessary support to the cartridge immediately behind it, and avoided the compression fault. Godsal also set the bolt as far back on the stock as he could in order to obtain a greater length of barrel within the rifle's overall length, which was another move to gain accuracy. This configuration inconveniently brought the rifle's magazine behind the trigger.

Godsal appeared again in 1916 with a heavy antitank rifle which used the same bolt action. This fired a .500in bullet from a necked-down .600in Express rifle cartridge case, which developed a high muzzle velocity. The rifle was fitted with a muzzle brake intended to reduce the recoil thrust on the firer's shoulder. None were ever adopted for service.

Hakim

This Egyptian service semiautomatic rifle was actually the Swedish Madsen-Ljungmann AG42 made in Egypt in the early 1950s. The principal changes in design from the Madsen original were the alteration to 7.92mm caliber from 6.5mm; the addition of an adjustment for the gas piston pressure to compensate for varying qualities of ammunition or, in emergency, to shut off the gas system completely and convert the rifle to a hand-operated weapon; and some alterations in the styling and contour of the rifle as well as the muzzle brake.

A smaller weapon, chambered for the Soviet 7.62mm short cartridge, was developed as the Rashid rifle, but few of these were made since it made better economic sense to buy AK47 rifles from Russia.

Hammerli

Hammerli SA of Lensberg, Switzerland, have long enjoyed the highest reputation for their production of target rifles and pistols. These range from off-the-shelf models suited to particular types of contest — for example the Olympic rifle match — to custom-built rifles and pistols specifically tailored to the requirements of individual marksmen. The appearance of many of these weapons is a trifle unsettling to anyone unfamiliar with the highest reaches of the target shooting world, since they lack the graceful lines and easy symmetry of the conventional rifle or pistol and, without pretence to appearance, are target-punching machines pure and simple. Adjustable shoulder stocks, thumb-hole stocks,

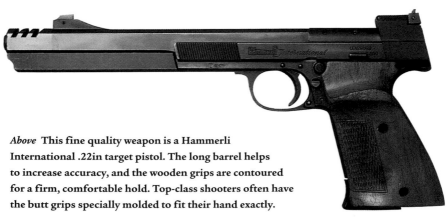

Above **This fine quality weapon is a Hammerli International .22in target pistol. The long barrel helps to increase accuracy, and the wooden grips are contoured for a firm, comfortable hold. Top-class shooters often have the butt grips specially molded to fit their hand exactly.**

set triggers, micrometer-adjustable sights, palm rests, and complex slings are all commonplace.

In recent years, principally for the American market, the company has produced a six-chambered revolver in Western style, known in its variant models as the Dakota or Virginian, and available in various calibers. To cater to the modern trend of heavy-caliber automatic pistol target

Above **Small caliber European self-loading pistols have proved very popular for precision target shooting. Top & lower left: .32in and .22in versions of the Walther GSP. Lower right : Hammerli 208.**

contest, the company has collaborated with SIG to produce a .38in caliber automatic pistol, the P-240, a weapon of the highest possible precision and quality.

Harrington & Richardson

Gilbert H. Harrington and William A. Richardson began manufacturing revolvers in 1874, and within a few years added shotguns to their products. Both died in 1897, but after being reorganized in 1905, the company has managed to continue to the present day, establishing a reputation as a major manufacturer of quality arms, produced at reasonable prices.

The company's first products were the usual cheap single-action solid-frame revolvers in .22, .32, and .38in rimfire calibers, but in 1887 they obtained patents for a double-action lock, and immediatly commenced the manufacture of a solid-frame revolver known as The American Double Action. Later models incorporated a patented Safety Hammer, in which the hammer had no projecting spur, but used a serrated rear surface which could be gripped by the thumb after the hammer had been started by slight trigger pressure, after which the hammer could be thumb-cocked. The "safety" term referred to in the name alludes to freedom from the danger of catching the hammer spur in the lining of a pocket when drawing the pistol in a hurry.

In about 1897 a line of hinged-frame revolvers was introduced as the Automatic Ejecting series, having the usual type of cam-actuated star plate in the cylinder which ejected the

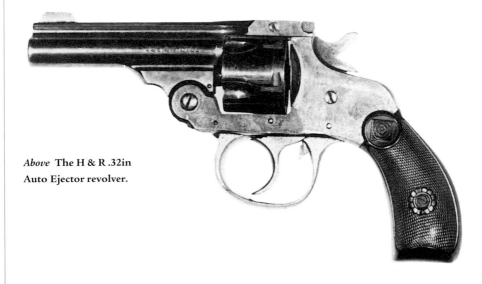

Above **The H & R .32in Auto Ejector revolver.**

Above **H & R .32in Hammerless
automatic pistol.**

empty cases as the revolver was
opened. An odd variant of this was
the Knife Model, a four-inch barreled
.32 or .38in pistol with a 21 inch
knife blade attached to the muzzle
and folded beneath the barrel when
not in use.

During the period 1910–1914,
the H&R Self-Loading Pistol was
marketed. This model was actually
the contemporary .25in Webley &
Scott Hammerless model, made
under license from the Birmingham
company, though there were one or
two differences in detail from the
original British model. A .32in pistol
was also made which, though based
on the Webley & Scott design, was
not a counterpart of any Webley
model. This appeared in 1913 and
was made until the early 1920s, but
neither of these pistols attained
much popularity in the United States,
and the company has never tried an
automatic pistol since then.

In the years following World War I,
new revolver designs appeared and
in 1929, a single-shot target pistol,
the USRA Model, achieved great
popularity and success in
competition shooting. Since 1945 the
company has produced a wide range
of solid and hinged-frame revolvers as
well as inexpensive shotguns.

Heckler & Koch

The Gewehr 3 (G3) from the Heckler & Koch stable uses a delayed blowback system of operation in which the opening of the breech is resisted by two rollers in the bolt assembly which engage in recesses in the barrel extension. Gas pressure on the bolt face, via the fired cartridge, forces the bolt head and rollers back. However, movement of the rollers is resisted by a shaped face in the bolt body, and thus the rollers force the heavy bolt body to the rear before they can allow the bolt head to open the breech. As is common with this type of action, the bolt opening is abrupt, and the chamber is longitudinally fluted in order to float the empty case on a layer of gas, and thus prevent it sticking in the chamber and failing to extract cleanly.

There are a number of variant models of the G3. The basic rifle is fitted with plastic butt and fore-end, is in 7.62mm NATO caliber, and has a 20-round magazine. The G3A3ZF model is fitted with a sighting telescope, while the G3A4 has a retractable butt-stock of tubular steel and the G3SG carries a variable-power range finding telescope and a lightweight bipod for use by snipers. The rifle's basic mechanism has also been incorporated into a machine gun design, available as the HK21 in belt-fed form or the HK1 1 in lightweight drum-fed form.

With the growing importance of the .223in cartridge, Heckler & Koch modified their rifle and machine gun designs to suit: the rifle became the HK33, the machine guns the HK21 and HK13 in this caliber. Finally the growing number of countries which

Right **The Heckler & Koch VP 70 is seen here with its holster/stock in position. The selector switch is set to the three-burst setting.**

Above **The up-to-date Heckler & Koch P9S uses roller locking of the breech similar to the mechanism used on H&K's rifles.**

had adopted the Soviet 7.62x39mm short cartridge led the company to produce the HK32 rifle and HK12 machine gun, both chambered for this caliber.

The gradual merging of the functions of the assault rifle and the submachine gun is to be seen in the

Heckler and Koch development. Their first step appears to have been to develop a shortened version of the G3, but in 9mm caliber, calling it the MP5. They then shortened the HK33 rifle, gave it a collapsible butt and a 40-round magazine, and called it the HK33K (K for *kurz,* or short) rifle, and then followed this with an even shorter version, which became the HK53 submachine gun. The difference between the submachine gun and the short rifle lies in the length of the barrel: the HK33 barrel is 15.3in (390mm) long, the HK33K 12.5in (322mm), and the HK53 8.2in (211mm) long.

Recently the company went into production with a sporting rifle, based on traditional lines but incorporating the G3 roller-locked action. Three variants were advertised: Model HK630 is for cartridges of 2.5in (63mm) length, HK770 for 3in (77mm) cartridges, and HK940 for 3.75in (94mm) cartridges. Broadly speaking, these cater to the 5/6, 7/8, and 9/10mm ranges of calibers, and the rifle can be chambered in any of the standard commercial calibers.

The company also developed a number of automatic pistols, ranging from the HK4, a blowback pocket model largely based on the pre-war Mauser HSc model, to the P9, P9S, and VP70 pistols which are intended principally for police and military. The P9 uses delayed blowback locking, the system uses rollers, and is obviously derived from the G3 rifle design. Chambered for the 7.65mm or 9mm Parabellum

cartridges, the P9 pistol has an internal hammer and normal single-action lock.

The P9S, on the other hand, uses a double-action lock with a thumb-operated cocking/de-cocking lever on the left grip. This model has recently been produced in .45in caliber as well as in two Parabellum calibers. The VP70 is a blowback pistol in 9mm Parabellum. The magazine holds 18 rounds. The pistol striker is cocked and released by trigger pressure and no safety catch is fitted. Moreover, by clamping a plastic butt-stock to the rear of the frame and grip, a fire-burst counter is brought into play which fires three shots for each pressure of the trigger, and converts the pistol into a form of quasi-submachine gun.

Above The Heckler & Koch G11 caseless rifle took 21 years to develop.

Below The caseless cartridges developed for the Heckler & Koch G11.

High Standard

This company was founded in 1926 to manufacture gun barrel drills and rifling equipment, but in 1932 they purchased the stock and tools of the bankrupt Hartford Arms Company.

Hartford had been making a .22in automatic pistol intended for target and recreation shooting — High Standard did continue to make this weapon, and merely changed the name. They later made sundry improvements to the design, and by the early 1940s had acquired a good reputation for inexpensive but accurate pistols.

During the war the pistol was produced as a training and recreation weapon for the United States Army, and a silenced version was provided for the Office of Strategic Services and for use by various clandestine organizations. In post-war years the line was expanded to produce a variety of pistols to suit particular applications. Thus, the Olympic ISU model is in .22in Short caliber, and tailored to the needs of the Olympic competition shooter, while the Dura-Matic model is a cheaper weapon intended for casual plinking and for carrying on hunting trips.

In the 1950s the company began producing revolvers, beginning with a .22in Kit Gun, a nine-shot model on a solid frame intended for field use. This was later replaced by the Sentinel series, which extended the range of available calibers to .357in Magnum.

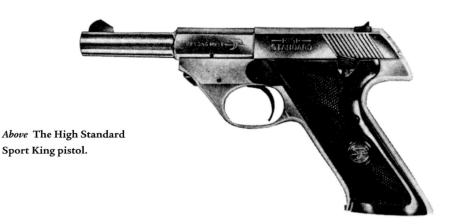

Above **The High Standard Sport King pistol.**

Above **Much target shooting is done with small caliber weapons such as this Hi-Standard model B .22in pistol.**

The second line of revolvers is based on the lines of the Colt Frontier. The Double Nine uses a nine-shot cylinder in .22in long chambering, and is supplied with a spare cylinder for the .22in Winchester Magnum Rimfire cartridge. Variations on this model, differing in barrel length, sights, etc., include the Durango, Longhorn, and High Sierra models.

Hino-Komura

The Hino-Komura pistol was patented in 1907 by Tomisiro Komura and K. Hino, having been developed in the aftermath of the Russo-Japanese War, when the Japanese Army had expressed a requirement for a self-loading pistol.

The design was unusual, and is best described as a blow-forward mechanism. The barrel was a moving component in front of a solid breech unit; on firing, the pressure on the base of the cartridge case, plus the drag imparted by the passage of the bullet up the rifling, caused the barrel to be impelled forward. The empty case was held by the extractor on the fixed breech, and was thus stripped from the chamber as the barrel moved away. A spring then returned the barrel, which collected and chambered a fresh cartridge from the butt-mounted magazine before coming to rest against the breech face. A firing pin was cocked during the barrel's movement, and the pistol was thus ready to fire the next shot.

The appearance of the pistol was equally odd, with a long, thin barrel, an exposed trigger without any form of guard, and a grip safety unit in the grip. About 1200 pistols in 7.65mm caliber are believed to have been made from 1907 to 1912, but they were not accepted for military service, and are now extremely uncommon.

Holland & Holland

Introduced in 1912, Holland & Holland's .375in Belted Rimless Magnum is regarded as one of the most effective medium-bore African cartridges. Holland & Holland still produce bolt action rifles on Magnum Mauser actions chambered for .375in H&H Magnum, as do a host of other manufacturers. The belted case added strength to the web of the cartridge, and many other high-performance proprietary and wildcat cartridges have been based on the .375in H&H case. Most ammunition manufacturers produce a .375in H&H load, with a 270 or 300 grain bullet. The lighter bullet has slightly more velocity and muzzle energy, at 2740 fps and 4500 ft lbs.

The .700in Express cartridge is designed for a double rifle produced by Holland & Holland, and is considered to be the most powerful big game cartridge available. The story behind the .700in Express began in 1974 when Holland & Holland ended production of .600in Nitro Express double rifles. They believed that the demand for such large

Below **Each .700in is handmade to an exact specification, the size of the action and overall weight being matched to the caliber.**

calibers was at an end, and with great fanfare announced the sale of "The Last H&H .600in Express." During the 1980s Holland & Holland were asked to build another .600in Express by Mr. William Feldstein of Beverly Hills, California. They refused, having made a commitment to the purchaser of the previous .600in rifle, saying that Feldstein's would be their last, and that unless he sold it back to them, they would not make any more. Feldstein then discussed the problem with Jim Bell of Bell Basic Brass, a specialty cartridge case manufacturer. They came up with the idea of a cartridge bigger than the .600in, and Holland & Holland then agreed to build rifles in .700in Nitro Express. The first rifle was completed in 1989, and weighed 19 lbs. The original cartridges fired a 1000 grain bullet propelled by 215 grains of IMR 4831 powder, to a velocity of 2020 fps and a muzzle energy of 9050 ft lbs. The gun is heavy but the well-balanced weight ensures that the recoil is not excessive — just over 136 ft lbs — less than that of some nineteenth century 4-bores.

Each rifle is handmade and produced to an exact specification,

Above **Holland & Holland .700in Nitro Express. The gun recoil is less than that of some nineteenth century 4-bores.**

the size of the action and overall weight being matched to the caliber. The method of construction is similar to that of a double-barreled side-by-side shotgun, but the action strength is improved to cope with the rifle's higher pressures. The double bite in the receiver, which holds the action closed during firing, is supplemented by an additional hidden bite between the ejectors which engages in the breech-face. A rounded thickening of the action known as the bolster (just below the chambers) adds rigidity, and the hammer springs are reversed in the back-action, sidelock trigger group to eliminate the need to remove metal in highly stressed areas.

Israel Military Industries

Apart from the popular UZI machine pistols, Israeli Military Industries also make a large gas-operated self-loading pistol, the Desert Eagle. This was produced for Magnum Research in the United States and was initially available in two versions which fired the popular revolver cartridges, .357in Magnum and .44in Magnum. The standard barrel on the Desert Eagle could be easily removed and changed for one produced by the

factory of up to 14 inches long. In .44in Magnum this significantly increased the power that could be generated from the cartridge with the combination of strong rotary locking breech and long barrel with no gas leakage apart from through the gas slide operating mechanism. In 1989 IMI produced the Desert Eagle in

Below **Very few pistols have worked well with .41 AE. However, one that does is the Jericho 941 (bottom) which can be converted to use 9mm Luger, in seconds.**

Above **The Desert Eagle was chambered for revolver calibers .357in Magnum, .41in Magnum, .44in Magnum.**

.41in Magnum and also chambered some barrels for .357/44in Bain & Davis, a wildcat cartridge.

In 1990 IMI announced an all-new rimless cartridge to be chambered in the Desert Eagle. .50in AE had anticipated ballistics of a 300 grain bullet traveling at 1632 fps and a muzzle energy of 1792 ft lbs. The cartridge and chamber dimensions had to be changed later in 1990 when

the American Bureau of Alcohol, Tobacco, and Firearms (BATF) declared that the bore of .50in AE was greater than .50 inches, and that all .50in Desert Eagles would be declared as destructive devices requiring special licensing. The result was a new .50 AE round with a smaller bore and bullet dimension, but the same ballistic potential. It will come as no surprise if a necked down version of .50 AE becomes available in something like .44/50in to facilitate the use of heavy .44 Magnum bullets at very high velocities and energies.

Iver Johnson

This company began in 1871 as Johnson & Bye, making cheap solid-frame revolvers. Bye sold his interest to Johnson in 1883, after which the company became the Iver Johnson Arms & Cycle Works. In ensuing years it produced firearms, bicycles, roller skates, airguns, handcuffs, and signal cannons.

The firearms products were inexpensive but sound shotguns and revolvers — the sort of weapons that were found in the rural communities in which the company's reputation has always been good. Their principal contribution to firearms design was the adoption of a Patent Safety Hammer which was invented by Andrew Fyrberg in 1896. In this mechanism an additional limb was fitted to the trigger, and the firing pin was no longer integral with the hammer but was mounted in the standing breech. When the hammer was at rest, a protrusion above the face abutted against the frame of the pistol and thus prevented contact between the hammer face and the firing pin. When the trigger was drawn back so as to trip and release the hammer, the additional limb was raised to interpose itself between hammer and the firing pin. When the hammer fell, it struck the top part of this limb, and the blow was thus transferred to the firing pin so as to fire the cartridge. Dropping the

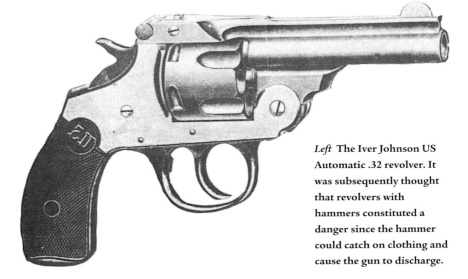

Left **The Iver Johnson US Automatic .32 revolver. It was subsequently thought that revolvers with hammers constituted a danger since the hammer could catch on clothing and cause the gun to discharge.**

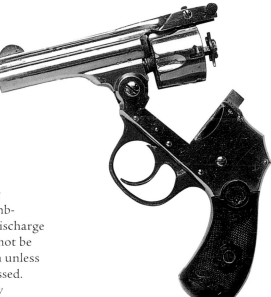

Right **Iver Johnson produced revolvers with the hammer enclosed within the body. These guns are referred to as "hammerless." Iver Johnson still manufactures firearms, but collectors are mainly interested in the company's early models.**

pistol, or letting the hammer accidentally slip during thumb-cocking, would not cause a discharge since the transfer bar would not be in place behind the firing pin unless the trigger were properly pressed.

The Iver Johnson company adopted the slogan Hammer the Hammer, together with an appropriate drawing, to publicize this device. This became a highly successful selling point.

Jäger

The Jäger pistol was made during World War I by Franz Jäger of Suhl. It was an unusual pistol, well in advance of its time since it was largely put together from stamped metal components, a technique which did not meet with general approval until the 1940s.

The pistol was built up from two steel sideplates which made up the butt and frame sides. Inside these plates locating pins held the parts of the firing mechanism, while two holes accepted a crossbar on the barrel breech, and positively located the barrel. The sideplates were held at the correct spacing by front and back straps held in place by pins and screws. The slide was a pressed-steel unit with the solid breech-block held inside by screws. The caliber was 7.65mm, and a butt-mounted magazine carried seven cartridges. It is believed that fewer than 6000 were ever made.

Jennings

Lewis Jennings was a little-known New England gunsmith who perfected a lever-action repeating rifle with a tubular magazine. This was the forerunner of the Henry and Winchester designs. Jennings took a rifle which had been designed by Walter Hunt of New York in 1849, and simplified the design to turn it into a commercially viable product.

Operation of the breech was by a ring lever beneath the stock, which unlocked and withdrew the breech bolt. A tubular magazine beneath the barrel contained up to 20 bullets, each of which had a recessed base containing the charge of powder. The muzzle of the gun was raised during the operation of the lever so that gravity caused a bullet to slide from the magazine on to a lifter controlled by the lever. On pulling the lever back, the breech bolt was driven

forward to chamber the cartridge. The hammer was now manually cocked, and a percussion cap placed on the nipple. When the hammer fell, the flash passed through the vent, through a passage in the bolt, and ignited the powder in the bullet's base.

The principal drawback was, of course, the lack of efficient sealing at the breech, but apart from that it was a mechanically sound weapon.

Kolibri

The Kolibri automatic pistol was made by Georg Grabner of Rehberg, and goes down in history as the smallest-caliber pistol and cartridge ever made. The design was based on a pistol called the Erika, which was already small; Grabner decided to make a miniaturized version and promote it as a self-defense gun for ladies, capable of being carried in any

Right **Another smaller company is that of Jennings of California, United States, who produce a selection of pistols, including a little .22in pocket pistol.**

Right **The Lilliput is so small that it is really more of a model than a real weapon. The Kolibri is smaller, at only 3mm caliber.**

handbag or purse. The 3-grain bullet produced about two foot-pounds of muzzle energy, which would probably have proved decisive against an enraged cockroach.

The Kolibri was produced in 2.7mm or 3mm calibers, the barrel being smooth-bored due to the expense and difficulty of rifling such a tiny caliber. A five-shot magazine went into the butt and the pistol was 65mm long and weighed 7.75oz (220 grams) fully loaded.

Krag-Jorgensen

Ole H. J. Krag was a first-class designer who took out numerous patents for rifle and pistol mechanisms; one of his last was for an automatic pistol which could be cocked and charged by one-hand action, a design very similar to that later perfected by Chylewski.

His name is, however, always united with that of Erik Jorgensen, the Works Superintendent of Kongsberg Arsenal and co-patentee of the Krag-Jorgensen rifle. This was a bolt-action magazine rifle with a unique form of magazine which

passed horizontally under the bolt, and then came up on the left side of the bolt-way. A trapdoor on the right side of the action could be opened, and the cartridges dropped into the magazine cavity. On closing the trapdoor a spring-loaded follower attached to it, then placed pressure on the loose cartridges and fed them through the magazine and up to the bolt-way where they were stripped off one at a time, as the bolt was manipulated. An advantage of this system was that the trap could be opened and the magazine topped up at any time, irrespective of whether the bolt was open or not.

The Danish Army adopted the Krag-Jorgensen rifle in 1889 and used it until 1945. The United States Army was the next to adopt it in 1892, though they soon replaced it with the Springfield. The Norwegians adopted it in 1894 and, like the Danes, used it until the end of the World War II.

Lampo

A palm-squeezer mechanical repeating pistol developed by Sgr. Catello Tribuzio of Turin in 1890. Chambered for the 8mm Gaulois cartridge, it could be concealed in the palm, the third finger engaging in a ring trigger, and the barrel protruding between the fingers and thumb. Pushing the trigger outward withdrew the bolt, and pulling it inwards closed the bolt, chambered a cartridge, and fired the pistol.

Lancaster

Charles Lancaster was a barrel-maker who set up in business in London in 1826 as a gunsmith. He died in 1847 leaving two sons, Charles William and Alfred, who continued the family business until 1860, when they split up. Charles William had developed a cartridge-loading shotgun in 1852 which enjoyed considerable success. It was a drop-down gun, the barrels being locked and unlocked by an under-lever, and it fired an ingenious cartridge which Lancaster designed. This had a cardboard body and a copper base perforated with four holes. The base was covered by a plain copper disk, and between the two disks was a thin coat of detonating compound. The shotgun's hammer drove a broad firing pin forward to strike the base of the cartridge, crushing the composition between the two copper surfaces, and causing the flash to pass through the four holes to ignite the powder inside the case.

Williams's protege, Henry Thorn, developed a useful single trigger mechanism which allowed the two

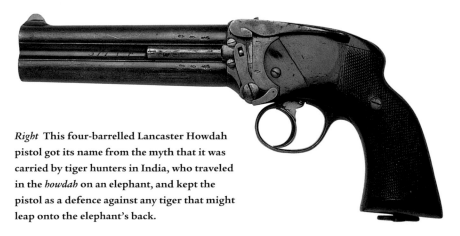

Right **This four-barrelled Lancaster Howdah pistol got its name from the myth that it was carried by tiger hunters in India, who traveled in the *howdah* on an elephant, and kept the pistol as a defence against any tiger that might leap onto the elephant's back.**

barrels of a shotgun to be fired in
succession from one trigger. He also
showed a liking for multi-barreled
guns. His four-barreled shotgun —
virtually two double guns
superimposed — found little favor
since it was a cumbersome and heavy
weapon, but his four-barreled pistol
was extremely popular with Army
officers. It had four .455in or .476in
barrels in a drop-down unit, with a
self-cocking firing mechanism which
fired the barrels in succession after
repeated pulls of the single trigger.

Lebel

Lebel, then Lt. Col. in the French
Army, designed a new infantry rifle.

Above **The French Lebel 8mm (top) was the
first small bore bolt military rifle to use
smokeless powder and a jacketed bullet.
The No. 4 rifle (bottom) in .303in was the
main British service rifle during and after
World War II.**

He applied himself particularly to the
design of the cartridge, realizing that
this was the most important part.

Fortunately, the chemist Vielle
had just perfected the first smokeless
powder, and Lebel alloyed this to a
drawn-brass cartridge case and a
small-caliber jacketed bullet to
produce the 8mm Lebel cartridge.
This remained the French standard
until the late 1920s.

Lefaucheaux revolver

Casimir Lefaucheaux was a Parisian gunsmith who, in 1836, developed a hinged-frame breech-loading shotgun which is now recognized as the ancestor of all double guns. The two barrels were joined side by side to a block of metal beneath the breech end. The block had a semicircular cutout at its front edge and a rectangular one at its rear.

The semicircular cut fitted around a cross-pin in the gun's fore end, and acted as a pivot to locate the barrels, while the rectangular slot received a crossbolt operated by an underlever to lock the barrels in place in front of the standing breech. The gun was chambered for a pinfire cartridge, the pins of which protruded through slots in the top edge of the chamber face and into the air above the breeches when the gun was closed. This enabled them to be struck by the falling hammers.

The hammers had to be cocked and pulled clear before opening the gun. The empty cartridge cases were then removed by using the pins. By modern standards, the gun was crude and unsafe, but it was a notable advance for its period, and cheap shotguns of this pattern were widely sold throughout Europe for the remainder of the nineteenth century.

Le Francais

All the Le Francais models follow the same basic design: a blowback automatic whose barrel is hinged to the frame in order to drop down in shotgun fashion when released by a side lever. This movement is also

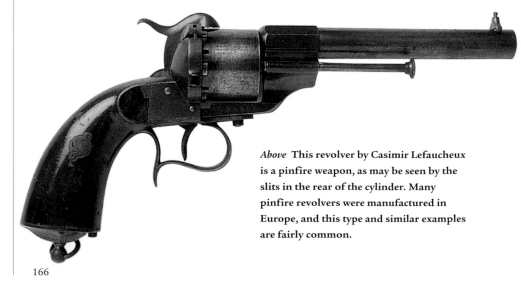

Above **This revolver by Casimir Lefaucheux is a pinfire weapon, as may be seen by the slits in the rear of the cylinder. Many pinfire revolvers were manufactured in Europe, and this type and similar examples are fairly common.**

Above **Another slightly unusual feature of Le Francaise was the forward-breaking movement of the barrel, although similar actions are found on other self-loaders.**

linked to the magazine, so that as soon as the magazine is withdrawn the barrel flies open, a certain method of ensuring safety while reloading. The breech block is conventional in appearance, but the return spring lies vertically in the front edge of the butt grip, and is linked to the breech by a bellcrank, one arm of which engages in the block while the other hooks to the spring. Firing is done by a self-cocking striker which is forced back against a driving spring by the first movement of the trigger, and then released to fire the cartridge. Upon firing, the breech block is forced back and the empty case is ejected from the chamber by residual pressure, as positive extraction was not possible.

The first Le Francais was a 6.35mm model which appeared in 1914 as the Modèle de Poche, followed by a 6.35mm Policeman model with a longer barrel. In 1928 a Military model chambered for the 9mm Long Browning cartridge appeared in the hope of a military contract, but although the French Army purchased some for trials, it was not adopted.

Liberator

In 1942 the United States Office of Strategic Services hit upon the idea of producing a cheap and expendable single-shot pistol which could be distributed to disaffected elements in enemy countries, and thus enable them to aggress their oppressors. For security's sake it was called the .45in Flare Projector. The design adopted for the Flare Projector was a stamped metal frame mounting a smoothbore .45in barrel, a hand-operated breech, and a hand-cocked striker. The butt was hollow and could be used to carry spare cartridges. In use, the breech was opened and a .45in cartridge inserted; it was then closed, and the striker cocked. Pulling the trigger discharged the shot, after which the breech was opened and the empty case ejected by poking down the barrel with a pencil or convenient twig. At short range it was quite effective. The name was changed to Liberator retrospectively when the gun was no longer confidential.

Lignose

The Lignose Pulverfabrik was a German company manufacturing explosives. In 1920 the company expanded, buying up smaller firms and forming a consortium, Lignose AG. Among the companies taken over was Theodor Bergmann Waffenfabrik of Suhl. Its output was henceforth known under the name of Lignose, and the pistols and sporting guns were marked accordingly. The best

Left **The Liberator was intended to play a part in the battles of World War II, to be dropped in quantities to various resistance groups fighting the Japanese in the Pacific. It is valued by some collectors as an oddity.**

Right This Australian-made self-loaded pistol is about 4.5 inches (11 cm) long, and it is known, appropriately, as Little Tom. This model is of .25in caliber, but a larger .32in caliber version was also produced.

known of the Lignose products was the Einhand automatic pistol.

These pistols were derived from the patents of Chylewski, which expired in 1921, following which the Bergmann company immediately began manufacture, but were soon affected by the Lignose move.

The special feature of the Einhand pistol was the ability to cock and charge the pistol with one hand. The front edge of the trigger guard could be drawn back, cocking the slide and, when released, allowed the slide to run forward to chamber a cartridge. Thus the pistol could be carried unloaded and safe, and then charged and cocked as it was drawn from the pocket. It was only successful in 6.35mm caliber. Although prototypes in 7.65mm and 9mm Short were made, the additional strength of

return spring needed for these more powerful cartridges required a much more powerful grip to cock the pistol, which made them impractical.

Little Tom

The Little Tom automatic pistol was designed and manufactured by Alois Tomiska, a Bohemian gunmaker. He patented it in 1908, producing models in 6.35mm and 7.65mm calibers. It was a simple blowback automatic, and was noteworthy for being the first successful automatic pistol to use a double-action lock in which the first shot could be fired by pulling through on the trigger to cock and release the hammer. He continued to make this design until the latter part of the World War I, after which he sold his patents to the Weiner Waffenfabrik of Vienna.

Mannlicher

Ferdinand Ritter von Mannlicher's particular interest was the repeating rifle and his first design, in 1880, was for a bolt-action rifle with three tubular magazines concealed within the butt. He quickly abandoned this and developed a box magazine below the bolt, then a tubular magazine below the barrel, and then a gravity-fed overhead magazine — all within two years. In 1884 he broke new ground by producing a bolt action in which the bolt handle was pulled straight back, without having to turn it, to open the bolt. In the following year he improved this design and added a box magazine loaded with a clip of cartridges. The clip remained in the magazine and the cartridges were fed out one by one until the last round had been fired, whereupon the clip was ejected past the open bolt.

Mannlicher's first success was the Austrian M1886 service rifle in 11mm caliber. This was a straight-pull bolt action, clip-loaded, whereby the clip dropped through a slot in the bottom of the magazine after the last cartridge had been chambered.

In 1887 he devised a turnbolt rifle with a revolving box magazine devised by Spitalsky, and then improved it by adopting a rotary magazine invented by Otto Schoenauer of the Steyr factory. These Mannlicher-Schoenauer actions were used extensively on sporting rifles and military weapons.

As early as 1885 Mannlicher had a recoil-operated automatic rifle working successfully. He later developed a number of delayed-blowback rifles, but such was the military conservatism of the time that none were met with approval.

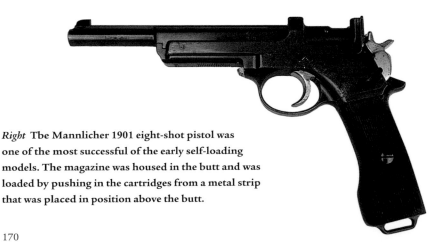

Right The Mannlicher 1901 eight-shot pistol was one of the most successful of the early self-loading models. The magazine was housed in the butt and was loaded by pushing in the cartridges from a metal strip that was placed in position above the butt.

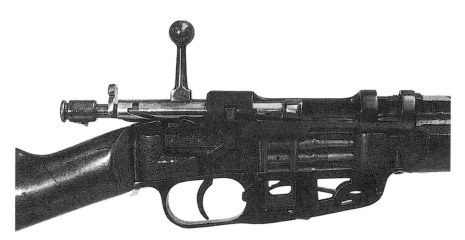

Above **The Mannlincher-Carano M1941, a typical bolt-action magazine rifle.**

His automatic pistol designs included a blow-forward model which achieved little success; a delayed blowback (the M1901) which is surely one of the most elegant and best-balanced automatic pistol ever made; and a locked breech model (the M1 903) with a box magazine resembling that of the Mauser.

Marlin

John Marlin was an out-worker in the gun trade in the 1860s. In the early 1870s he began making cheap solid-frame rimfire revolvers and single-shot pistols, and then moved on to include single-shot falling-block rifles. His activities prospered, and in 1881 the Marlin Firearms Company was formed, and the lever-action rifle was introduced.

This rifle had a tube magazine below the barrel, and superficially resembled the contemporary Winchester, even though the breech action was much different. Instead of using a toggle mechanism, the lever moves the breech block by direct linkage, and the block is locked in place by a vertical locking strut which, actuated by the lever, moves up and enters a recess in the lower side of the block. The lever also operates the usual sort of cartridge lifter. This rifle, in a variety of calibers, has remained the mainstay of the company ever since, though in 1898 shotguns were added to the firm's range.

In about 1887 a double-action hinged-frame revolver went into

production, but contemporary reports gave an unfavorable opinion of this weapon, and the company discontinued it in the late 1890s, in order to be able to concentrate on shoulder arms.

Mars

The English Mars is one of the most powerful, complicated, and rare pistols in history. It was designed by Hugh Gabbett-Fairfax of Leamington Spa. In 1895 Gabbett-Fairfax patented a long-recoil pistol with rotary magazine, of which one specimen is still known to exist, but he then changed his design to accomodate a conventional butt magazine. In 1897 he offered the design to Webley & Scott, but they decided not to adopt it, though they were willing to manufacture it for Gabbett-Fairfax to sell.

Accordingly, he organized the Mars Automatic Fire-Arms Syndicate in 1901, but shortly after this Webley changed their minds and returned the designs. Manufacture was then arranged with an unknown Birmingham gunsmith, and pistols were subsequently made, placed on sale, and submitted for military trial. After exhaustive tests the pistols were turned down — since the Syndicate had gambled on military acceptance, this refusal in 1903 brought about their liquidation as well as Gabbett-Fairfax's bankruptcy. A fresh Mars Automatic Pistol Syndicate was then formed and a few more pistols made, but this venture failed in 1907, and the Mars vanished. The novelty of the Mars — and its downfall — lay in its mechanism and in the ammunition which Gabbett-Fairfax designed for it.

It was a long-recoil pistol of considerable ingenuity. On firing, the barrel and bolt, securely locked, recoiled about two inches along the top of the frame, cocking the external

Above **Marlin's lever actions with tubular magazines handle cartridges as powerful as their own .444in Marlin. The Model 336 shown is chambered for .30in.**

hammer as they came to rest. The bolt was then revolved to unlock it from the breech, and the barrel ran back to the forward position. As it did so, the empty cartridge case was extracted, and a mechanical ejector knocked it clear of the feedway. During the recoil stroke, a cartridge carrier withdrew a cartridge backwards from the magazine, and lifted it up to align with the chamber. All this happened in a split second, so that the firer could relax his grip

on the trigger and prepare to take the pressure for the next shot. This pressure released the bolt, which ran forward, chambering the cartridge, and then revolving in order to lock into the breech. At the same time, the cartridge carrier dropped down and grasped the next cartridge in the magazine.

Over the years, the Mars pistol was produced in four calibers, namely the 8.5 mm, 9mm, .36in, and .45in calibers, all of which fired special bottle-necked cartridges of exceptional power. The 9mm, for example, fired a 156 grain bullet at 1650 feet a second in order to give a muzzle energy of 943 foot-pounds.

Right **Mars automatic pistol in .45in caliber.**

Mauser

In spite of the astronomical number of Mauser rifles adopted throughout the world, the actual design changes to the original were comparatively few. The Model 1871 service rifle was a single-shot turnbolt weapon in 11mm caliber. The bolt was locked when the bolt handle was turned down in front of a shoulder in the action body; the firing pin was withdrawn as the bolt opened, and fully cocked on the closing stroke. A manual safety catch was fitted to the rear end of the striker.

With the arrival of repeating rifles, Mauser developed a conversion of the 1871 design which used the same

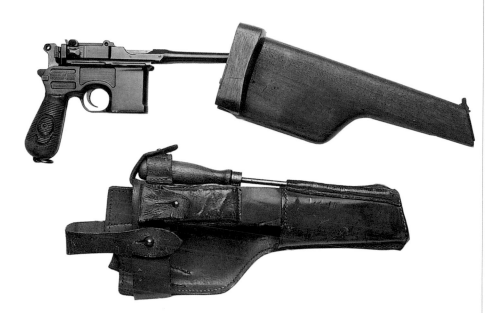

Left **Mauser's bolt action Model 86SR sniper rifles are available with laminated or synthetic stock.**

Above **The 9mm Mauser Broomhandle is shown here with its wooden holster and rather complex leather carrying rig.**

bolt, but added a tubular magazine below the barrel along with the usual type of bolt-actuated cartridge lifter. This was adopted in 1884, but the German Army wanted a "packet-loading" system, and in 1888 the Commission Rifle which used the Mannlicher system of clip loading therefore went into service. The bolt action was much as before, but with a vitally important alteration in the method of locking, which was now done by two opposed lugs on the bolt head which engaged in recesses in the

breech face as the bolt was rotated. (Mauser had developed this system of locking on a 9.5mm rifle supplied to Turkey in 1875.)

Mauser was far from pleased at seeing his rifle displaced by what he felt to be an inferior design, and he set about developing his own packet-loading rifle. Instead of the currently popular retained clip, he chose to use a five-round charger which was lodged in the boltway. The five cartridges are swept out and into the magazine by thumb pressure.

Above The butt of this Mauser Broomhandle is clearly marked with a red 9, indicating that it is chambered for 9mm cartridges.

Above A Mauser Broomhandle pistol and stock. This version is the Schnell Feuer, and the small plate at the side is a selector switch. When it is in one position, the pistol will fire a single shot each time the trigger is pressed.

(A distinction must be made here: correctly speaking, a "clip" becomes part of the magazine, and the gun cannot be operated without it, whereas the "charger" is only a cartridge-holder, though now is often refered to as a "clip") A box magazine below the bolt took the cartridges and forced them up by a spring-loaded arm. This system, together with a one-piece bolt with forward locking lugs, was used first in the

M1889 Belgian service rifle. The next major improvement came with the M1893 Spanish Army rifle in which the magazine became a more compact unit concealed within the rifle stock, instead of being a metal box in front of the trigger guard.

In 1898 the German Army discarded the Commission Rifle in favor of a Mauser design, the Gewehr 98. The principal change here was the incorporation of a third, rear, locking lug on the bolt. There were no further major changes in Mauser rifle design after this; subsequent Mauser bolt-action rifles developed by the Mauser company or by other countries — for example, the Belgian and Czech 1924 models.

Having perfected the bolt action, Mauser turned to the development of automatic rifles. Various systems were explored such as the short recoil, long recoil, turning bolts, and locking by flaps and cams, but few designs ever went beyond the prototype stage. The German Army tested the various designs without accepting them, but in 1915 took a number of Mauser's last designs into use as the Flieger Selbstlader Karabiner 1915, and issued them as aircraft observer's guns.

Intial development of Mauser pistols began badly, with a single-shot weapon in 1877 which achieved limited production. In the following year he produced the Zig Zag revolver,

Above Made by Mauser, the HSc .32in pistol is shown here. This is a double-action weapon, which means that it can be carried safely with a live round in the chamber. For a rapid first shot, the trigger is simply pulled right back, and the shot is then fired.

Right **The Broombandle shown with the stock in position. When it was used as a carbine, it was a very accurate weapon, and when it was firing automatically it was easier to control. On full automatic fire all handguns are difficult to hold firmly, and tend to spray shots.**

which gained its name from the grooving on the outer surface of the cylinder. As the pistol was cocked, a pin in the frame moved back and forth and, riding in the zig-zag groove, rotated the cylinder. Mauser had hopes of a military contract since the Army was anxious to adopt a revolver, but his design was turned down as being too expensive and complicated, and the Army settled for the more primitive Reichsrevolver.

In 1886 Mauser produced designs for a mechanical repeating pistol with

a tubular magazine below the barrel, and a finger-actuated mechanism of watch-like complexity. It is unlikely that any were ever made.

It was not until 1896, with the Mauser Military Pistol, that he achieved anything resembling success in the handgun field, and it must be said that this pistol was not his idea, but had been developed by the Superintendent of his factory, Herr Federle. Although it was to sell by the millions in later years, the Military (and its variant successors) was never adopted as an official service arm by any major power.

The Military relied on a reciprocating bolt inside a square-

Left **Mauser 1896 and 7.63mm Mauser cartridge. The finely machined and carefully designed Model 1896 was nicknamed the Broomhandle because of its distinctive grip.**

section receiver. This was locked to the breech by two heavy lugs which entered the bottom of the bolt, since the pistol fired a powerful 7.63mm cartridge. Ten rounds were charger-loaded into a box magazine ahead of the trigger, and a wooden holster-case could be clipped to the butt to form a shoulder-stock, after which the pistol could perform as a type of carbine. It was invariably beautifully made and finished, and in spite of an unprepossessing appearance it is, in fact, a comfortable and accurate pistol to shoot.

The variant models principally encompassed changes in barrel length, sights, and safety catch. However during World War I, the German Army placed a contract for 150,000 pistols chambered for the 9mm Parabellum cartridge, the only time the pistol was ever made in other than the 7.63mm caliber.

Above Another unusual feature of the Zig Zag pistol is the upward-breaking barrel, which is released by the ring catch set near the front. This model was introduced in 1878.

Above The Zig Zag pistol is distinguished by its cylinder rotation system. A movable stud set in the frame engaged with the sloping groove, and cut into the cylinder as it moved foward, turning the cylinder. When a shot was fired, the stud returned to its original position via the straight slot.

The only other major change came in the early 1930s when, in response to competition from Spanish gunmakers who were marketing imitation Mauser pistols, Mauser produced a full-automatic version which, when fitted with its butt-stock, became a species of submachine gun.

The first Mauser pocket pistol was introduced in 1910. This was a blowback automatic in 6.35mm caliber, and was followed in 1914 by a 7.65mm version. These were rather larger than might be expected for pocket weapons of such calibers, but they were robust and well-made weapons which were adopted in numbers by various continental police forces. In 1934 the design was brought up to date by adopting

Above Right **A close view of the top of a Mauser 1896 pistol. The beautiful blued sight slide and the general high quality of the workmanship are clearly seen.**

Above Left **Mauser's 1898 type rifle bolt set the standard for others to follow. The .303in No. 4 rifle bolt has lugs at the rear rather than at the front on the Mauser. The Tikka bolt has both for extra strength.**

a better-shaped grip, but this model was eclipsed by the 1938 Model HSc, a 7.65mm pistol of modem appearance, with double-action lock, obviously produced in response to the competing Model PP by Walther.

The vest pocket market was also catered for by two Westentaschen pistols in 6.35mm, one appearing in 1918 and the other in 1938.

Nagant

Brothers Emile and Leon Nagant were gunsmiths of Liège. Emile appeared first, manufacturing the usual sporting guns, saloon rifles, and single-shot pistols in the 1870s. His first success was the 9mm Belgian service revolver of 1878.

In 1883 the Russian Rifle Test Commission announced a competitive trial to select a new service rifle. Nagant presented his design alongside another competitor, S. I. Mosin (1849–1902), a Russian artillery officer. After much deliberation, the Commission decided to construct a rifle using the bolt action designed by Mosin allied to the controlled box magazine from the Nagant design. The final result was the Model 1891 rifle.

Leon's claim to fame comes from the gas-seal revolver which he patented in 1892.

The long-standing objection to revolvers was that, in order to permit the cylinder to turn, it was necessary to have a finite gap between the face of the chamber and the rear of the barrel. Some propelling gas was bound to leak through this gap, which in theory reduced the theoretical efficiency of the pistol.

In the Nagant revolver the cylinder was allowed to move back and forth in the frame, its movement governed by a linkage from the hammer. The face of the chamber was bell-

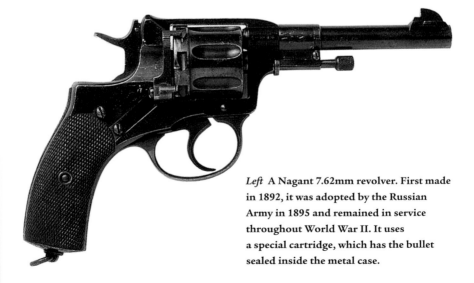

Left **A Nagant 7.62mm revolver. First made in 1892, it was adopted by the Russian Army in 1895 and remained in service throughout World War II. It uses a special cartridge, which has the bullet sealed inside the metal case.**

Right **The Russian M1895
revolver is loaded through the side gate.**

mouthed, and the rear of the barrel
tapered. In addition, the cartridge
was specifically designed for the
revolver and the bullet was concealed
within an elongated cartridge case,
the mouth of which was slightly
bottle-necked.

The Russian Army adopted it as
their 1895 model, and it remained in
use with them until the end of World
War II.

Nagant continued to make and sell
gas-seal revolvers on the civil market
in the 1890s, but in 1900 the Russian
government purchased all rights to
the patent, and put the pistol into
production at their Tula Arsenal.

Nambu

Major (later General) Kirijo Nambu's
pistol was a locked breech pistol in
8mm caliber. Its lock took the shape
of a pivoted block beneath the bolt.
Although superficially resembling
the Parabellum, this mechanism
bears closer affinities to the Italian
Glisenti, and was probably actually
copied from it. The breech-block
return spring was set to one side in a
tunnel in the frame, which gave the
pistol a lop-sided appearance. The
only safety device was a grip safety
set located in front of the butt.

Parabellum

Parabellum was the telegraphic address of Deutsche Waffen & Munitionsfabrik of Berlin and was also applied as a trade name to various weapons. Of these, the most famous and important is undoubtedly the pistol developed by Georg Luger and marketed as the Parabellum, though universally it was called the Luger.

The DWM company had taken over the manufacture of the pistol along with the Löwe company factory, and Georg Luger then collaborated with Borchardt to improve its design. The principal change came with the modification of the toggle breech mechanism so that the toggle was broken by the interaction of two finger-grips striking a ramp in the fixed pistol frame after a short recoil. This threw up the center of the toggle, and broke the resistance to the recoil force of the cartridge. Thereafter the breech block was driven back as the toggle rose, so as to extract the fired case and, propelled by a leaf spring concealed within the pistol butt, then returned to strip a cartridge from the magazine, and chamber it. A striker within the block was cocked during this latter movement.

Above **Alloy frames are now common in modern service pistols. Models from the Beretta 92 series in 9mm Luger have been adopted for military and police use in the United States and France.**

After several trials, the first Luger pistol was adopted by the Swiss Army in May 1900, the pistols being chambered for a bottle-necked 7.65mm cartridge known thereafter as the 7.65mm Parabellum. The

Above **The Luger P'08 pistol design introduced the 9mm Luger cartridge, which is now one of the most popular mid-powered pistol cartridges in the world. In 1991, Mitchell Arms produced the first stainless-steel replica of the P'08.**

pistol was actually given the name Parabellum by DWM in the spring of 1901.

The most common objection to the pistol was to the 7.65mm bullet, since military opinion at that time inclined to calibers in the order of .45in (or 11 mm) in order to achieve the greatest shock power with a single shot. Luger therefore opened out the neck of the 7.65mm case to turn it into a straight case, and inserted a 9mm bullet. In 1902 this caliber was offered as an alternative. After more trials, the German Navy adopted this caliber in 1904.

In 1905 a major design change occured with the adoption of a coil spring in the butt to return the toggle, instead of the original leaf spring.

In 1908 the adoption of the Pistole '08 by the German Army set the final seal on the Parabellum's acceptance. In 9mm caliber with a 4in barrel, the quantity demanded was far in excess of DWM's capacity, and additional pistols were made by the Government arsenal at Erfurt. During these years an additional model, the Long '08, was adopted; this had a 200mm barrel, long-range sights, and a large snail magazine which was capable of carrying 32 rounds, and therefore extended below the butt.

Below **.45in ACP has marginally greater notional muzzle energy than 9mm Luger, but both hollowpoint and ball .45in ammunition have proved far more effective in gunfights than 9mm.**

Above **This specimen is a Naval Luger, which was first adopted in 1904. The models vary in detail, and apparently, similar guns can fetch very different prices.**

In addition a wooden butt-stock could be fitted to the weapon, turning it into a type of carbine. It was issued to artillery units, machine gunners, and to a number of coastal motorboat crews. The wooden butt-stock was a feature of many of the Parabellum designs, most pistols being fitted with a shoe at the rear of the butt grip into which this stock fitted.

When World War I ended, the manufacture of Parabellum pistols came to a halt; under the provisions of the Versailles Treaty, DWM were forbidden to manufacture them.

In 1930 the production of the Parabellum was reorganized; at that time DWM was in the hands of a holding company, Berliner Karlsruhe Industriewerke (BKIW), who were also controlling Mauser. A policy of rationalization led the production of all small arms to be concentrated in the Mauser factory at Oberndorf,

leaving the DWM plant for other things. As a result, the Parabellum machinery and production line was moved to Oberndorf early in 1930. Although Mauser was now solely responsible for production, the pistols still carried the DWM monogram on the toggles.

The Swiss government continued to use the Parabellum as their standard pistol, but due to difficulties in obtaining supplies during the War, in 1918 they set up their own production facilities in the Arsenal at Bern, continuing to produce the last (1906) pattern which had been purchased from DWM. By 1928 they had come to the conclusion that at a unit cost of SF220 the Parabellum was too expensive. However because they liked the design, they set the Arsenal technicians the task of modifying it so as to reduce the manufacturing cost. This was done by eliminating many cosmetic machining steps; knurling on the finger grips was omitted, the frame contours were made more simple, the front strap of the butt made straight, and so forth. This brought the price down by 30% and the new design went into production in 1929 as the Pistole 06/29. About 30,000 were made before production finally ended in 1947.

In the years after the war the demand for Parabellum pistols seems not to have abated. In the 1960s negotiations opened between the American Interarm company and Mauser, with the result that new machinery was assembled and

in 1970 a new Parabellum pistol appeared. This was based on the Swiss 06/29, the simplified design. It was then followed, in 1973, by a model based on the Pistole '08, with the swelled-out front edge to the grip. The quality and finish is of the highest class, but the problems of manufacturing a complicated design in relatively small quantities are reflected in the high price.

Pedersen

During World War I J.D. Pedersen was responsible for designing the Pedersen Device (or Automatic Pistol) Caliber .30in M1918. This was a self-contained bolt and return-spring unit which could be installed into the action of a standard Springfield rifle after removing the bolt. The unit consisted of a tubular receiver, bolt, return spring, chamber, and barrel;

Below **One of the best known holsters is the one that was used for the Luger '08 pistol.**

Above **This fine example of the Artillery Luger is complete with leather bolster, shoulder board and snail drum magazine.**

the barrel was externally the same size as the standard .30 rifle cartridge, so that it fit inside the chamber of the rifle, while the remaining parts sat in the boltway. An obliquely fitted overhead magazine slotted into the device, and the rifle was thus transformed into a species of submachine gun. The ammunition fired was a special .30in short cartridge, slightly longer than a normal 7.65mm ACP pistol cartridge. The object behind this was to permit front-line troops to convert their rifles into fast-firing weapons which could then be fired from the hip during the advance across No Man's Land.

In 1923, after M1918 was withdrawn, Pedersen went to work for Springfield Arsenal and developed a delayed blowback rifle using a toggle-joint breech mechanism. The angles of the toggle unit were carefully calculated so that instead of positively locking the breech, as in the Maxim and Borchardt toggles, this one slowed down the blowback action. The rifle was in .276in caliber, but, like most blowback weapons, used bottle-necked cartridges, and gave trouble with extraction. Pedersen developed a dry-wax method of lubricating the cartridges which cured extraction problems. Unfortunately, lubricated cartridges are not a solution which military authorities approve of, and although the Pedersen rifle was an excellent design, it was rejected for service.

Reichsrevolver

The Reichsrevolver of 1879 was designed to specifications laid down by a Committee formed by the Prussian Army, and charged with producing a modern weapon to replace the single-shot pistols of the time. Two models were eventually produced, the M1879, sometimes called the Cavalry or Troopers model, and the M1883, or Infantry or Officers model. The basic difference is that the M1879 had a 7.2in barrel, while the M1883 had a 5in barrel. Both were single-action, gate-loaded, solid frame revolvers. A safety catch was fitted on the left side of the frame.

The adoption of such an antiquated design as late as 1879 has always been considered to have been a triumph for conservatism over technical advance. The American Smith & Wesson Russian model, a top-break revolver with automatic extraction, had been introduced in 1870, and there were any number of commercial revolvers which pointed the way to more modern designs. In spite of all this, the Reichsrevolver became the standard issue, and it remained so until the adoption of the Parabellum pistol in 1908.

Remington

The Remington concern was founded in 1816 in Ilion, New York, by Eliphalet Remington, a barrel-maker, and his sons. In 1902 the company was merged with the Union Metallic Cartridge Company to become Remington-UMC Co., and finally it was given its present name, the Remington Arms Co. Inc.

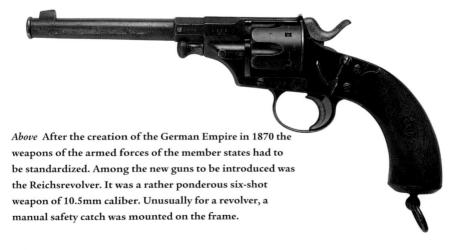

Above **After the creation of the German Empire in 1870 the weapons of the armed forces of the member states had to be standardized. Among the new guns to be introduced was the Reichsrevolver. It was a rather ponderous six-shot weapon of 10.5mm caliber. Unusually for a revolver, a manual safety catch was mounted on the frame.**

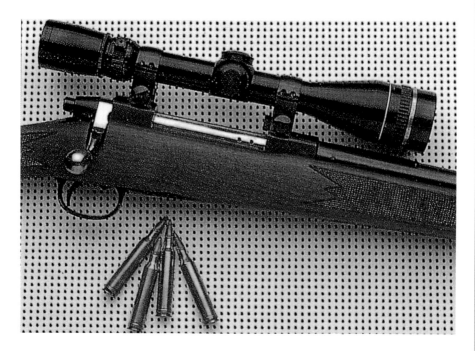

One of the very first in the Remington line was the "rolling block" rifle. This rifle originated with a patent by Leonard Geiger in 1863, and was subsequently modified by Joseph Rider, a designer working for Remington. It was a breech-loader, for metallic cartridges, and used a pivoted breech block which swung up into place behind the chamber. The rear surface of the block was curved in such a way as to mate with a curve on the front face of the hammer, which was then pivoted directly behind the block. The

Above **Tikka Model 65 chambered for 7mm Rem Magnum.**

cartridge was inserted into the chamber and the block hinged up, a spring holding it snugly against the base of the cartridge. When the trigger was pressed, the hammer fell, and during its fall the curved face on the hammer breast passed beneath the curved rear of the block so as to support it when the recoil force tried to push it back as the cartridge fired. It was a positive, safe lock, capable of withstanding heavy loads.

Above and Right **Remington's production of percussion revolvers, one of which is shown here, began in 1857, and it made a variety of weapons ranging from pocket revolvers to large .44in weapons for military use.**

Their next major step was the adoption of the Lee bolt action and magazine in 1880. The company developed several military and sporting rifles around the Lee system.

John M. Browning became associated with Remington at the turn of the century, and for them he produced a semiautomatic rifle mechanism which was first offered in .22in and then in more powerful calibers. This was followed with a slide-action repeating shotgun, and these proved to be profitable designs which, with periodical refinement, have survived to the present day.

In the pistol field their earliest memorable design was the 1874 .44in New Model Army revolver. This was a single-action six-shot, gate loaded weapon intended to compete with the Colt Frontier of 1873. It can be recognized by a peculiar triangular web beneath the barrel. It was a first-class arm, but never managed to achieve the popularity of the Colt.

After the collapse of the original Remington company in 1888, pistol manufacture tapered off as Remington were not able to compete with the flood of cheap revolvers into the market. The wisest course was therefore to abjure the pistol field and concentrate on shoulder arms, which they did outstandingly well. The exception to this was a single-shot target pistol which they produced from 1891 to 1909 and which was popular with competition shooters of the day.

During World War I, they employed J. D. Pedersen who produced a design of automatic pistol in .45in caliber.

Model 51 of 1919 is a pocket pistol variation of the Pedersen design. It was a fixed-barrel automatic with a slide enveloping a separate breech

block. On firing, the block recoiled for a short distance, pushing the slide back, until it was stopped by an abutment on the frame. The slide was free to continue to the rear, and after a further short movement, a shaped surface inside the slide lifted the breech block away from the abutment so that it could recoil with the slide; the barrel remained stationary throughout. On the return stroke the block was closed up against the breech and then, by the shaped surfaces in the slide, forced down so as to be aligned ready to strike the abutment on the next shot. In 9mm Short caliber, and later produced in 7.65mm, the Remington Model 51 was a high-quality weapon and notable for being well-shaped for instinctive shooting. But it was an overcomplicated design for the caliber it used and

manufacture was discontinued in 1934.

In 1963 the idea of using powerful pistols for hunting was beginning to gain ground in the United States, and Remington were quick off the mark to produce a weapon specifically designed for this. The notable XP-100 was a shortened version of their current bolt-action rifle mechanism allied to a 10.5 inch barrel, and all installed on a nylon-based plastic stock. The fore end of the stock was hollowed out so that weights could be installed to balance the weapon for the individual owner, and the sights were fully adjustable. It was chambered for the .221in Remington Fireball cartridge, giving 2600 feet a second with a 50-grain bullet, and being capable of producing one-inch groups at one hundred yards range.

Rigby

John Rigby & Co., the famous London gunmaking company, was originally established in Dublin in 1735. A London branch of the company was established in 1865 and the Dublin premises were subsequently closed.

Below Rigby introduced the .416in Rigby cartridge for their rifles in 1911. By the time their 1924 catalog was produced it had established a reputation as an accurate and powerful big-game round.

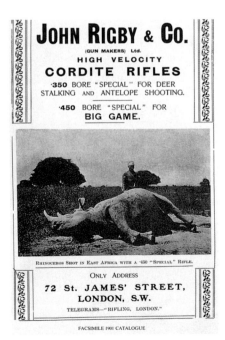

JOHN RIGBY & CO.
(GUN MAKERS) Ltd.
HIGH VELOCITY
CORDITE RIFLES
·350 BORE "SPECIAL" FOR DEER STALKING AND ANTELOPE SHOOTING.
·450 BORE "SPECIAL" FOR
BIG GAME.

RHINOCEROS SHOT IN EAST AFRICA WITH A ·450 "SPECIAL" RIFLE.

ONLY ADDRESS
72 St. JAMES' STREET,
LONDON, S.W.
TELEGRAMS—"RIFLING, LONDON."

FACSIMILE 1901 CATALOGUE

Much of Rigby's production includes bolt-action sporting rifles, but they also produce double rifles as well as their sidelock side-by-side shotguns. Like Holland & Holland, the rifle actions are much stronger than those of shotguns.

In addition to the traditional .600in and .577in Nitro Express double rifle calibers, Rigby also chamber their doubles for high-performance bolt-action rifle cartridges such as .416in Rigby and .458in Win Mag.

Rigby introduced the .416in Rigby cartridge in 1911 for their Mauser Magnum action rifle. The .416in Rigby can be used for big game, and fires a 410 grain bullet to 2371 fps (723 mps) for an energy of 5100 ft lbs (6911 joules). Ruger's Model 77 Magnum is the only American rifle manufacturer chambered for just .375in H&H and .416in Rigby.

Rigby also produced a .775in (10-bore) rifle. The smokeless 10-bore rifle cartridges used can fire a 1100 grain (71.3 g) bullet at 1500 fps (457 mps) for a muzzle energy of 5497 ft lbs (7449 joules).

Right and Above Right **Intricate inlaid engraving is often requested on fine British-made rifles like Rigby's .275in and their square bridge .375in.**

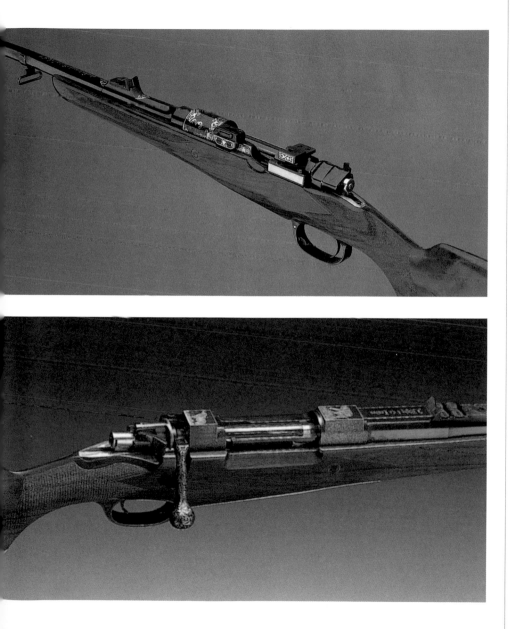

Ruger

William B. Ruger took out his first patents for an automatic pistol in 1946. He then set up a company, Sturm, Ruger & Co., and in 1949 began manufacture of his pistol. It was an instant success, being inexpensive, reliable, and accurate. With this project underway, Ruger saw that there was a great demand for single-action Western-style revolvers which had been unsatisfied since Colt had ceased to manufacture their Frontier model.

Ruger therefore designed and began production of a single-action revolver, not an imitation of the Colt but an original design which was well-engineered. The Ruger revolvers were such a success that Colt was forced to reconsider their decision, and many other companies went into the single-action revolver business, though few had Ruger's success.

The company then moved into the manufacture of double-action revolvers for defense and police use, to the manufacture of a single-shot falling-block sporting rifle, to a semiautomatic carbine in 5.56mm caliber (the Mini-14), and later, to a double-barreled, over-and-under 20-bore shotgun of excellent quality.

The bedrock of all this was the original Standard .22in automatic pistol. This uses a fixed, exposed

Above **Ruger chambers its Model 77 Magnum rifle for just two calibers, both British, .375in Holland & Holland and .416in Rigby.**

barrel with a tubular receiver in which a bolt reciprocates in blowback action. Firing is by an internal hammer, arranged to give a short lock time. Variations in barrel length and weight are provided for target shooting purposes. The single-action revolver line began in 1953 with the Single Six, based on the lines of the Colt Frontier but with internal changes, such as the replacement of leaf springs by coil springs and the incorporation of a floating firing pin in the standing breech.

In 1968 the Gun Control Act was passed in the United States and in 1971 the United States Treasury laid down stringent rules as to the safety of revolvers. Modifying the hammer face so that it normally rested on the frame, clear of the firing pin, and adding a transfer bar to the lockwork, was enough to bring the Ruger pistol

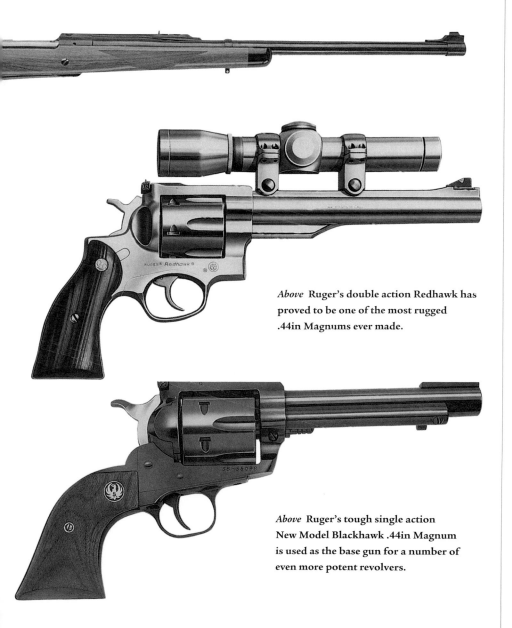

Above Ruger's double action Redhawk has proved to be one of the most rugged .44in Magnums ever made.

Above Ruger's tough single action New Model Blackhawk .44in Magnum is used as the base gun for a number of even more potent revolvers.

into line with the new rules. Now the hammer could only touch the firing pin if the trigger was properly pulled back for deliberate firing, which forced the transfer bar up behind the firing pin and thus transmitted the hammer blow to the pin when the hammer fell. This is comparable to the Iver Johnson Hammer, the Hammer safety, and the Colt Positive Safety Hammer designs. In 1973 Ruger revolver designs were modified to this new standard, and were thenceforth known by the additional designation of the word "Super" in front of their names.

The Number One rifle was introduced in the middle 1960s, and uses an underlever to lower a vertical sliding breech block. This is not an innovative system, since similar mechanisms were in use almost a century ago, but it is well-engineered and immensely strong, capable of handling the heaviest sporting loads.

The Mini-14 carbine is a semiautomatic weapon resembling the United States Army's M1 carbine, though it has a slightly different gas operation system. Chambered for the 5.56mm cartridge, it was originally restricted to police use, but has since been placed on the open market.

Left **Custom pistol smiths have chambered other revolvers such as Ruger Super Readhawk for .454in Casull.**

Right **Ruger's new P85 pistol uses a swinging link to effect delayed blowback, as John Browning did in his original Colt 1911.**

Sauer

The firm of J. P. Sauer & Son in Suhl was founded in 1751, beginning Suhl's rise to eminence as a gunmaking center. For the most part the company was concerned with the production of sporting arms, being particularly noted for drillings, or three-barreled guns in which two

Below **A German 7.65mm pistol, Model 3811, manufactured by Sauer & Sohn. Approximately 200, 000 were made during World War II, and a large number have survived. The design is excellent, and the hammer can be cocked by using the side-mounted lever.**

barrels are smoothbored for shot and the third, below, is rifled in a suitable sporting caliber. From time to time the firm was given contracts for military weapons, producing Mauser rifles, and being involved in a consortium for the production of the Reichsrevolver.

Sauer's first commercial pistol was the Bär, the repeating pistol patented by Burkhard Behr, in 1898. This remarkable weapon, in 7mm caliber, sold quite well in the early 1900s as a personal defense weapon, one virtue being that it was very slender and could be easily concealed. Eventually sales began to fall due to competition

Above **Carried by many units of the German Army during World War II, the Sauer & Sohn Model 38H was ingeniously made. It was capable of being fired in either single or double action.**

from pocket automatic pistols, and Sauer decided to go into this field, buying a design from George Roth. This design then became the Roth-Sauer model.

Like most of the Roth/Krnka designs, the Roth-Sauer was too complicated and used the long-recoil system of operation which was superfluous since it was chambered for a very weak 7.65mm cartridge.

Having survived these essays with other people's designs, Sauer then developed one of their own. The pistol appeared in 1913 and was a

7.65mm blowback featuring a fixed barrel, annular recoil spring, lightweight tubular slide, and a separate breechblock retained in the slide by a knurled screw cap at the rear end. A seven-shot magazine fitted in the butt and the pistol was striker-fired.

Shortly after World War I the design was repeated in 6.35mm caliber, but this model was only produced for a short time, being too complicated a manufacturing task in such a small caliber. It was replaced by a more conventional design, the

WT (*westentaschen*, vest-pocket) model, which generally resembled the Baby Browning but still had the Sauer separate breechblock pinned into the slide.

In 1930 a new 7.65mm model was introduced, still to the same basic design as the 1913 version, but with some small detail improvements. This was widely adopted by Police and similar bodies, and became known as the *Behordenmodell* (Authorities' or Official Model). This remained in production until 1937.

The Official Model was replaced the following year by a completely

Below **The SIG-Sauer SSG2000 Precision sniping rifle is based on the proven bolt action of the Sauer 80/90 rifles.**

The P220 pistol is a heavy-caliber locked breech model available chambered for .45in, .38in Super, 9mm, and 7.65mm Parabellum cartridges. Breech locking is by a heavy lug on top of the barrel allied to a shaped cam beneath the breech, basically the SIG-Petter system. The breechblock, in Sauer fashion, is a separate component pinned into the slide. An external hammer is used and is allied to a double-action lock. The same cocking lever as used on the 38H.

Another model, the P230, is a fixed-barrel blowback with annular recoil spring; this too has an external hammer, double-action lock, and side cocking lever. It is chambered for a new cartridge, the 9mm Police, slightly larger than the 9mm Short but not as powerful as the 9mm Parabellum. It would appear to be derived on similar lines to the Soviet 9mm Makarov round, a cartridge intended to extract the maximum power from a blowback pistol.

new design, the Model 38H. (The "H" indicates *hahn*, which signifies the use of a hammer instead of a striker.) This was potentially one of the best pocket pistols ever made. It was a fixed-barrel blowback automatic with a double-action lock — a control lever on the left side of the frame which allowed a cocked hammer to be eased down onto a loaded chamber, or an uncocked hammer to be cocked. In conjunction with the double-action lock, it gave the user full control over the options of firing double- or single-action at all times.

Savage

The Savage Arms Company of Utica, New York, was begun in 1894 by Arthur Savage, who designed a naval torpedo that was adopted by Brazil. He then designed a lever-action sporting rifle and set up the company to make this rifle.

Christened the Model 95, the action of this rifle differed from other lever-actions — that of the Winchester and Marlin — in being truly hammerless, streamlined, and in using a rotary magazine. This latter feature allowed the use of pointed bullets in a lever action rifle for the first time; previous lever actions all used tube magazines beneath the barrel, and the close proximity of the bullet point to the cap of the cartridge in front was a dangerous feature and one which militated against the use of modern ammunition in these rifles. The Savage design changed this; it also made for a more slender and graceful weapon. The breech closure was done by a block which was thrust forward by the lever action and then lifted so as to lock into mortises in the receiver wall, and was supported there by the lever during firing. The breech block contained a striker and spring.

Small improvements were made in the Model 99 (of 1899), and since then the design has remained relatively unchanged. It was followed by slide-action and bolt-action .22in rifles in 1903, and in 1907 the company went into the production of an automatic pistol.

The Savage automatic pistol was largely the work of Major Elbert H. Searle, a former ordinance officer.

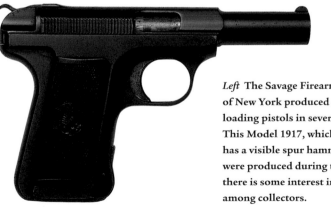

Left **The Savage Firearms Company of New York produced a number of self-loading pistols in several calibers. This Model 1917, which is 32in caliber, has a visible spur hammer. Over 14, 000 were produced during the 1920s, and there is some interest in these weapons among collectors.**

Right One of the competitors in the trials held in the United States to select a self-loading pistol for the Army was a .45in pistol made by the Savage Arms Company. Although it was not selected, the company produced similar pistols, including this .32in example.

The design used a rotating barrel which was linked to the slide by a lug riding in a shaped groove. When the pistol was fired, the lug held barrel and slide together, but reaction between a lug under the barrel and a cam track in the frame rotated the barrel through 5 degrees and unlocked the slide, after which it recoiled in the usual way. The opening of the breech was delayed by the reaction of the bullet as it passed through the rifling, which resisted the turning movement of the barrel. Although the barrel and slide may be locked at the instant of firing, they certainly do not remain locked for very long afterwards, and the Savage is therefore considered more of a delayed blowback pistol, in spite of Searle's claims to a locked breech.

Savage was working on this design in 1906 when the United States Army canvassed for automatic pistols for the 1907 trials, and they made one in .45in caliber and entered it. It survived the trial, and a further 230 were delivered for troop trials between 1909 and 1910, but the decision was taken to adopt the Colt and so the Savage .45in was dropped. Meanwhile the commercial model in 7.65mm had been marketed in 1907. Minor changes in design occurred in 1915 and 1917, and it remained in production until 1926.

Following World War I the company continued producing sporting guns, pistols, and ammunition. It also manufactured huge numbers of .30in and .50in Browning machine guns and over a million Lee-Enfield rifles for the British Army during World War II. At the end of the war it returned to the production of sporting arms.

Smith & Wesson

The Number One revolver from Smith & Wesson was a .22in rimfire, single-action, with the frame hinged at the standing breech in order to tip upwards when a latch at the front of the lower frame was released. The cylinder could then be slipped from its arbor, the empty cases punched out by means of a rod protruding beneath the barrel, reloaded, and replaced.

The American, which appeared in 1870, was a heavy .44in rimfire revolver. It was a hinged-frame model with simultaneous ejection of the spent cases as the barrel was hinged down, a system based on patents of W. C. Dodge and C. A. King and held by the company. In that year the Russian Army decided to adopt the Smith & Wesson design, but with some small modifications. The most important change was in the cartridge, which the Russians redesigned to make more accurate.

The Smith & Wesson pocket revolvers were hinged-frame models in .32in and .38in caliber, with ribbed barrels and a simplified auto-ejecting mechanism.

In 1887, they scored a first with their New Departure model. This was the first hammerless revolver to be successful, and it had the additional feature of a grip safety lever, which protruded at the rear edge of the butt. The pistol did use a hammer, but this was concealed from view by a rising frame, and thus there was no projecting hammer spur to catch in a pocket when the pistol was being drawn.

In 1896, the company adopted the swingout cylinder form with a .32in Hand Ejector model. The cylinder was locked in place by a pin which passed through the arbor, and anchored into the standing breech. The pistol was then opened by pulling forward on the ejector rod, which extended beneath the barrel. It was not a very strong design, and in 1899 a .38in Hand Ejector was produced which had a thumb operated catch on the frame which pushed the cylinder-locking pin out of engagement. This still wasn't perfect, and in 1902 the design was improved by placing a locking lug under the barrel into which the front end of the ejector rod engaged, thus locking the cylinder assembly at both ends.

In 1908 a final refinement was introduced, a third locking lug at the

Right **This Smith & Wesson .38in revolver is fitted with a trigger shoe. This is a little device used by some target shooters to afford a firmer touch on the trigger. By the side is a speed loader used to load six rounds in one movement.**

Above The long barrel on this .22in Smith & Wesson single-shot pistol indicates that it is primarily a target weapon. It is a top break pistol and the first examples of this weapon were made on modified revolver frames, but later the frame was altered.

Left Although the name Smith & Wesson immediately suggests an American weapon, this example was made by the firm primarily for Russia. The company was contracted to supply thousands of revolvers for the Russian armed forces.

fronι of the cylinder aperture, into which the crane arm (which supported the cylinder) locked. The same thumbcatch, forcing the arbor pin forward, actuated all three locks, but as might be imagined, the manufacture and adjustment of the three locking surfaces was very precise and difficult. This system was introduced on the .44in Hand Ejector of 1908, which inevitably became known as the Triple Lock model. More properly, it was called the New Century model, and many authorities claim it is one of the finest revolvers ever made.

Above **To survive on the streets, modern handguns use plastics, aluminum alloys, and stainless steel in their construction.**

In 1917 the United States Army demanded a .45in revolver which could fire the standard .45in automatic pistol cartridge. Since it was normal practice of Smith & Wesson to design a slight step in the chamber, against which the mouth of the cartridge case abutted, there was no difficulty in loading and firing such rimless cartridges, but as a result, the ejector had nothing to grip and would not remove the empty cases. This was solved by developing a half-moon clip which held three rimless cartridges. Two such clips could be dropped in to load the chamber, the revolver fired and opened, and the ejector then bore on the clip so as to eject the cases. This model became the United States Army's M1917 revolver. Later on, an ammunition maker produced a special .45in cartridge with a thick rim, so that the special clips were no longer required.

Below **The .41in Magnum cartridge was intended for law enforcement, but it proved to have too much recoil for many.**

In 1913, the company purchased the French patents of Clement. This used a blowback system, with a square bolt working in a slot in the body, but it was an awkward and expensive design to make, and matters were complicated by the fact that Smith & Wesson chose to make it in the odd caliber of .35in, producing their own ammunition to suit. In 1924 they produced a slightly simplified version which chambered the usual .32in auto pistol cartridge, but it was still more expensive than its rivals, and less than a thousand were sold as a result.

In 1934, the company originated the Magnum idea in pistols. Their

first model was the .357in Magnum Hand Ejector, an extremely strong and heavy revolver chambered to

Below .45in ACP has an enviable reputation as a powerful sporting and defense cartridge. Smith & Wesson make stainless-steel double-action pistols to fire it. The full size Model 4506 (direct) has a magazine capacity of eight rounds, the compact Model 4516's magazine holds seven plus one in the chamber.

accept a special cartridge of higher than usual power. Although the bore was the same as the normal .38in revolver, the notation was .357 in order to distinguish the superpower cartridge from the ordinary .38in (which, in fact, is .357in in caliber). Moreover the new cartridge had a longer case so that there was no danger of loading it into an ordinary .38in revolver chamber due to the case fouling the chamber step. This

Above **Two versions of the Smith & Wesson Model 27 .357in Magnum revolver. The example with the 6 inch (15 cm) barrel is designed primarily for target work.**

weapon proved to be very popular since not only was it powerful, but it was also extremely accurate, and apart from an interval during the war years, has continued in production. Other Magnum loadings pioneered by the company are in .41in and .44in caliber. The Smith & Wesson company also has a sound reputation in the shotgun field. They now make both slideaction and automatic guns.

Springfield

Among the most famous of the early Springfield designs was the Trapdoor rifle of 1868. This was a conversion from muzzle-loading on much the same lines as the contemporary Albini and Snider conversions. The rear of the barrel was cut away and a hinged block installed. This could be lifted, hinging forward, to allow a .45in cartridge to be inserted into the breech. A firing pin inside the breech block was aligned with the cartridge when the block was closed, and an external hammer fired the weapon. Not only was it popular with the Army, but it also achieved a considerable following among hunters and trappers for its efficient simplicity.

The first Springfield rifle was produced in 1900, using a new cartridge which proved not to be very efficient. This was redesigned, and at the same time the rifle was shortened to become one of the first of the short rifles, doing away with the old-style division of long rifles for infantry and carbines for mounted troops. The final design was issued in 1903 as the Rifle US M1903, but it was called Springfield, which is the name that has remained. Another improvement appeared in 1906 with the adoption of a pointed bullet, since which time the basic United States Army cartridge has invariably been referred to as the .30.06, relating its caliber and year of introduction.

The Mauser design of the time was slightly modified in the Springfield rifle as the magazine cut-off was built

Above For the sport of IPSC Practical Pistol combat target shooting, a factory customized pistol can be bought from Springfield Armory. The model illustrated uses a 9mm slide, but is chambered for the Major power cartridge, .38in Super.

Above **The Omega pistols from Springfield Armory have a universal slide and breech which can accommodate a number of different calibers on a basic 1911Al frame.**

in to the bolt release catch; a two-piece firing pin was adopted, and other minor changes made.

Contrary to often-expressed opinion, no Springfield rifles were issued to the British Home Guard during World War II. They received numbers of M1917 Enfield rifles, and in many cases these were shipped from Springfield Arsenal (the markings on the packing cases led to the misnaming of the rifles). The rifle was subsequently known as the P17.

Steyr

The Osterreichische Waffenfabrik Gesellschaft of Steyr was founded in 1853 by Werndl who, after visiting the United States to study production methods, established a 15-workshop complex to convert muzzle-loading rifles into Werndl breech-loaders for the Austro-Hungarian Army. After converting 80,000 rifles, he obtained orders to manufacture 100,000 breech-loaders, and after that the orders came in profusion. By 1880 the Steyr factory's output exceeded that of any other rifle plant in the world, 13,000 rifles a week leaving its gates.

Steyr was the principal manufacturer of Mannlicher rifles and pistols. The Austrian Army

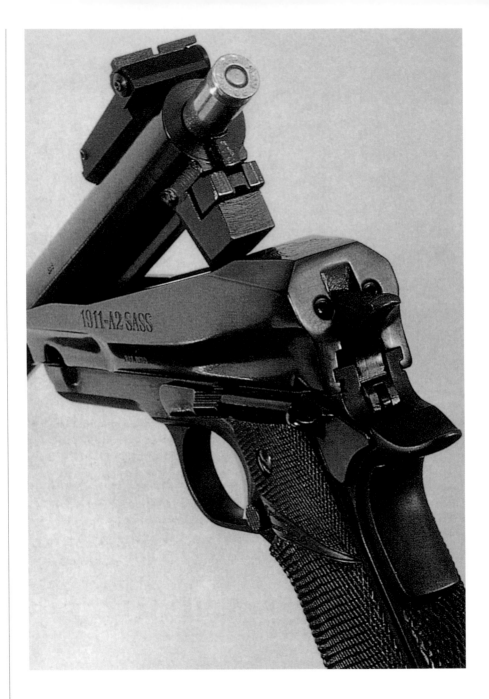

Above **Springfield Armory produce a number of versions of the 1911A pistol, the smallest being their Compact .45in.**

Left **Springfield Armory's 1911-A2 SASS conversion turns a 1911A1 self-loading pistol into a break-top single shot that can fire rifle cartridges.**

sniping rifle, the SSG, is an up-to-date Mannlicher-Schoenauer, using the same turnbolt and rotary magazine that was developed at the turn of the century. The modern aspect is reflected in the stock, which is entirely of plastic. The SSG is an extremely accurate weapon, and civil versions for hunting are available in various calibers.

The Steyr pistols were a mixed lot; the first products were to the designs of Pieper, a gas-seal revolver very similar to the Nagant, and produced in small numbers in the middle 1890s. When the design did not prosper, the factory turned to automatic pistols. It had already worked on the Schonberger and Mannlicher designs, and now turned to the pistols developed by Roth.

For a pocket pistol it went back to Pieper, this time to Nicolas, and produced numbers of the tip-up barrel pistol in 7.65mm caliber prior to World War I. After the war it abandoned the pistol field, and it was not until the 1970s that a new design appeared, the Pistole Pi18. This is an unusual design of delayed blowback pistol, the delay being obtained by tapping a small portion of gas from the chamber, and leading it to the interior of the slide. Here it enters an annular expansion chamber and brings sufficient pressure to bear on the slide to resist the opening movement due to blowback. The lockwork is double-action, and the pistol can be converted to full-automatic fire; in this case it is used with an over-length magazine and a short butt-stock, turning it into a compact submachine gun.

Walther

The early Walther pistols were all blowbacks of simple construction and great quality, but it was not until the advent of their PP Model in 1929 that they really displayed anything outstanding. This introduced the double-action lock to common usage, and was closely followed by the PPK model, a smaller version for plain-clothes police.

In the early 1930s the German Army let it be known that they were looking for a new design to replace the service Parabellum. Walther first put forward a 9mm Parabellum version of the PP, but this was refused. The next attempt was the Model AP (*Armée Pistole*), a locked

breech weapon using a wedge beneath the barrel to lock slide and barrel together. This incorporated the double action lock of the PP, and had the hammer concealed in the frame and under the slide.

Next came the Model HP (*Heeres Pistole*, which also means "army pistol") in which the hammer had been moved to an external position. This was approved, and became the Pistole 38.

Other notable models include the pre-war Olympic Modelle, a long-barreled .22in target pistol which gave an excellent performance in the Berlin Olympics, and the post-war OSP (or Olympic Schell-feuer pistole), also in .22in caliber and also

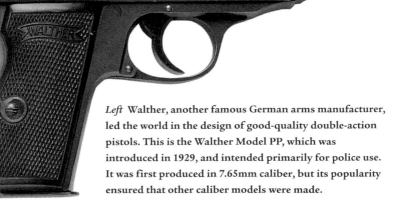

Left Walther, another famous German arms manufacturer, led the world in the design of good-quality double-action pistols. This is the Walther Model PP, which was introduced in 1929, and intended primarily for police use. It was first produced in 7.65mm caliber, but its popularity ensured that other caliber models were made.

Right **Two versions of the 9mm Walther Pistole .38in or P38 were developed in 1938. The P38 was a replacement for the Luger 08.**

a target arm of the highest standard. This was followed by the PP Super pistol.

Webley

In 1867 Webley's first official service contract was acquired for the Royal Irish Constabulary (RIC) model. This was also widely adopted by police and military forces throughout the Empire. It was a short-barreled heavy-caliber weapon, extremely reliable and robust, and was eventually made available in several variant models and calibers, remaining in production until the end of the century.

In 1877 the company began production of a hinged-frame self-extracting revolver incorporating the Pryse patents; these covered the rebounding hammer and cylinder lock, and the revolver also incorporated a double-bolted frame lock which kept the revolver securely locked against the power of the heaviest charges.

The first Mark 1, adopted as the British service pistol in 1887, was a six-shot hinged-frame weapon in .442in caliber with a 4 inch barrel.

The Mark 4 of 1899 introduced the .455in cartridge and this continued through until the adoption of the Mark 6 in 1915. In addition to service revolvers the company also produced a wide variety of pocket revolvers in hammer and hammerless styles and in .32in and

.38in calibers from the 1870s onwards.

In the 1890s the automatic pistol appeared on the scene, and Webley were offered the Gabbet-Fairfax Mars pistol. After some trial with this, they refused to adopt it as their own, and their designer Mr. W. J. Whiting began working on his design. His first experimental model appeared in 1903, chambered for a powerful .455in rimless cartridge specially developed for it. The aim was to produce a heavy military weapon, although it was some years before the design was perfected.

Meanwhile, a blowback automatic in 7.65mm caliber was introduced in 1906, a model which was adopted by the Metropolitan Police in 1911, and following this was widely adopted

Above **The Webley-Fosbery model was initially based on the Mark IV revolver which were chambered and regulated for the service .455 cartridge.**

in Britain as a police pistol.

By 1909, the locked-breech design had been perfected and was offered to the Royal Navy. It was also marketed in .38in ACP chambering, and a version in 9mm Browning Long caliber was bought by the South African Police. The Royal Navy adopted the .455in version in May 1913 and retained it until after World War I. These pistols are heavy and angular, and rely on inclined keys on the side of the breech mating with inclined grooves in the slide; as the slide and barrel recoil, the barrel is permitted to move downward so that the engaged faces come apart and allow the slide to move separately. One unusual feature is that the magazine can be slightly withdrawn from the butt and held locked in a special notch. The pistol can then be hand-loaded and fired as a single-shot weapon, keeping the full magazine in reserve. When needed, a blow of the hand sends the magazine up into the top position, and the pistol then functions as a self-loader once more.

The Webley-Fosbery automatic revolver was derived from the invention of Colonel G. V. Fosbery. VC. Fosbery's original idea was to make a revolver in which the barrel and cylinder were movable units,

sliding across the top of the butt frame on recoil, and thus cocking the hammer. Since the hammer controlled cylinder revolution, this automatically rotated the cylinder, and thus the pistol was ready for the next shot. The system worked, but it was clumsy, and with the aid of Webley's designers, Fosbery next adapted it to the standard Webley revolver and changed the system of operation. He cut grooves in the exterior of the cylinder which engaged with a fixed peg in the pistol frame. As the barrel and cylinder recoiled over the frame, the peg forced the cylinder to revolve one-twelfth of a turn. On the return movement, another one-twelfth of a

Right **A small bar set at the top of this Webley WE 320 could be pushed back to lock the hammer in such a way that it could not be cocked The hammer was shrouded to reduce the chances of it being snagged on clothing.**

turn was made, bringing a fresh chamber into line with the barrel.

Winchester

In 1855, Oliver F. Winchester purchased some stock in the Volcanic Arms Company. However, the Volcanic rifle was not a commercial success, and in 1857 the company failed. Winchester, though, was convinced that the Volcanic design was capable of improvement, and hired Tyler Henry to redesign the Volcanic rifle. Henry developed a .44in rimfire cartridge and then modified the rifle mechanism to suit, producing the Henry rifle in 1860.

In 1866 a new rifle appeared, the Winchester Model 1866. This used much the same mechanism as the Henry, but was improved by the adoption of King's magazine loading feature, in which the cartridges were pushed into the rear of the magazine through a trap in the side of the action body, instead of being dropped into the front of the magazine tube.

In 1873 came the Winchester 73, which introduced center-fire ammunition in the lever-action Winchester rifle for the first time.

In the 1870s the company employed Hugo Borchardt for many years. He developed some excellent revolver designs, but no orders were forthcoming. According to legend, the idea of producing a revolver was dropped as a result of a "gentleman's agreement" with Colt, that Winchester would stay out of the revolver business if Colt left rifles alone.

Another famous name allied with Winchester was that of John M. Browning. However, the two parted ways in 1900, when Winchester refused to pay Browning royalty for an automatic shotgun. Winchester factory had done such a good job of drawing up Browning's patent specification, that it took the company's engineers ten years before they could develop a shotgun that evaded the patent.

During the First World War the company was involved in manufacturing Enfield rifles for the British and United States governments. After the war it diversified into hardware, electric torches, refrigerators and innumerable other fields in order to keep the war-expanded plant occupied — among other things, it made radiators for Rolls-Royce. But this venture was not a success, and with the depression years adding to their problems, the company went into receivership in 1931. It was eventually bought out by the Western Cartridge Company, and reorganized once again, this time with the intention of keeping to the manufacture of guns and ammunition. The company's fortunes gradually improved during the 1930s, and continue to the present day.

During World War II the company put forward a gas-operated military automatic rifle using a short-stroke piston arrangement invented by

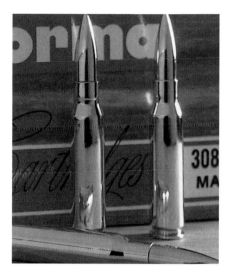

Above Norma have also made their own .308 Norma Magnum cartridge.

David Williams, one of their designers. Although favorably tested by the United States Marines and by the British Army, it was not pursued largely because the Americans were committed to the Garand, and the British were reluctant to try a completely new rifle during wartime.

Nevertheless, the basic principle of the weapon was used when the United States Army demanded a short carbine for its supply troops, and this became the United States Carbine .30 M1. This is still in popular use throughout the world, and has been widely copied.

Above In addition to ammunition, Winchester make their Model 70 Sporter and Super Express bolt action rifle for their own and other calibers.

Index